UNVEILING THE ADDICTED HEART

Jon S. Gieber MS, CADC II

Amber Geiger
3630 NE 10th Avenue
Portland, OR 97212
amber@ambergeiger.com

Cover illustration by Faith Geiger.

Contents

Acknowledgements

"Why me?" I often ask myself. Why did I wake up from my addiction? After I realized on that early Sunday morning that the paranoia telling me that those men had shot guns and that they were coming to kill me was from the cocaine, after I realized that I was hopeless by myself and that I needed help, I turned to you. You understood that I was desperate. You didn't scoff at me like the psychiatrist who told me I sounded fine to him, that I was somehow trying to "rip off the system," who yelled at me before finally slamming down the receiver in my ear. You didn't dismiss me like one counselor who thought that coming in to chat with him once a week would be enough. You didn't burden me by suggesting that LSD now and then would be my way out of addiction. You listened to me, you believed me. You understood how many times I had tried to stop and that I could never stay stopped. You understood how addiction had corrupted my soul yet you loved me anyway. You knew that the one thing I needed the most was to understand and accept one simple truth: I am an addict. Over 22 years ago you helped me accept this truth; for this, I am eternally grateful. Your face changed during that time: Tom Mann, Jim Creasey, Brad Kearns, Sam Graves, Joann Breeden, and Jo Hodges. Yet your message was constant: accept your powerlessness and reclaim your soul; this is the foundation upon which to build your recovery.

Thank you from the bottom of my heart.

This book is dedicated to Tom, Jim, Brad, Sam, Joann, and Jo. It is also dedicated to all those counselors who remain solid in their conviction that their primary job with addicts is to help them accept their powerlessness and reclaim their souls.

A special thank-you to my parents, Larry and Maureen Gieber, who had the love and wisdom to put me in the hands of those who could help me the most. Their ability to accept and love me despite my cocaine addiction was pivotal in my becoming a recovering person.

A final thank-you to my beautiful wife, Janey Gieber. Her constant encouragement, her wisdom, and her soulfulness have all greatly contributed to my evolution as a man, which includes having the courage to write this manual.

Introduction

Who should read this book?

Helping addicts recover from their disease can be a very humbling and difficult endeavor. There are no magic words, recipes or devices that insure recovery. It can be a very messy business. Counseling addicts is an endeavor that requires a willingness to give witness to often-horrible traumas (albeit second hand) on a daily basis; the raw, gut-wrenching exposure of the realities of addiction can be gruesome. Counselors, who work with addicts will inevitably be confronted with the death of a client they have cared for, hoped for and believed in. Sometimes the death is due to overdose, or a medical complication related to their use, or perhaps the addict's despair is too great for them to manage and they turn to suicide to escape their pain. It takes courage, compassion and conviction to work as an addiction counseling professional.

Helping addicts recover from their disease can also be a very exciting and rewarding. Addicts shrouded in the despair and demoralization of their disease often wake up to the reality that the primary source of their problems is their use of mood altering drugs and that they can recover by simply not using. The relief that many addicts experience when they are able to accept their addiction is often instantaneous. Hopelessness is replaced by hope; a guilt and angst give way to forgiveness and grief. Addicts can heal quickly, reclaim their dignity and re-engage in their lives. Helping addicts recover can be a sacred experience as we bear witness to the re-birth of a human being.

This book is intended for anyone who wishes to help people who suffer from addiction: ministers, teachers, social workers, nurses, physicians, and coaches. Simply put, anyone who has contact with addicts is potentially in a position to help them save their own lives. While this text is specifically developed with the addiction counseling professional in mind, the set of knowledge and skills described can be useful to anyone who dares to respond to the pain of an addict. No one should underestimate his or her ability to help change the world for another. A single voice, a gentle, loving willingness to respond to another's pain, can truly provide the opening to a path of healing.

What qualifies the author to write this book?

Jon Gieber is the Department Chair of the Alcohol and Drug Counselor Department at Portland Community College. He has been a full time faculty member since 1987. He entered the addiction counseling profession in 1981. In addition to his teaching duties, he has a private practice where he works primarily with addicts. He has served as a consultant and provider to the Oregon Board of Medical Examiners Health Professional Program since its inception in 1990. He has earned a BS degree in Psychology and a MS in Counseling from the University of Oregon. He is a Certified Addictions Counselor Level II (Oregon). He has been a recovering addict for over 22 years. Many of his family members are also recovering addicts.

The addiction-specific counseling approach he proposes in this text is not based not upon an ivory tower analysis devoid of real world experience, nor does it arise exclusively from the realm of personal experience, but it comes from a cauldron of over twenty years experience working with addicts (including his own recovery), coupled with careful scrutiny of available scientific information. Most importantly, the ideas in this book have been tested with real clients who suffer from the disease of addiction.

How will this book specifically help counselors, help addicts?

The intent of this manual is to synthesize the real world experiences of addicts and the scientific understanding of addiction into a counseling approach that is specifically targeted to help addicts address what is referred to in the Twelve Step programs as the first step, "We admitted we were powerless over alcohol—that our lives had become unmanageable" (Alcoholics Anonymous).[1] This counseling approach, called the Anchor Point System (APS), specifically facilitates the exploration of how powerlessness and unmanageability are experienced in the individual addict's life. The APS is a respectful and gentle counseling approach that is simple to understand and employ. The APS honors the reality of addiction and the healing potential of each human heart; it is a path that can be used to help wake the addict up from their prisons of self-deceit and self-destruction.

The APS can be used in individual, couple, family and group applications. This book is intended to be a training manual for anyone who works with the addicted population. This manual delineates step-by-step the APS. The APS is simple to understand and implement, but, like most counseling techniques, it takes considerable time and practice to master. Creation of videotapes using role-plays that allow the counselor to practice the prescribed skills greatly accelerates mastery of the APS.

How is the APS different from other counseling approaches?

The APS was developed by combining elements of human experience and scientific inquiry. The core identifying characteristic in the APS model of addiction is loss of control. Loss of control (LoC) is defined as using a substance more than intended or using it despite negative consequences. In the current addiction-specific trainings and counseling approaches, it is rare that they acknowledge LoC as an essential feature of addiction that must be embraced if addiction is to be appropriately understood and treated.

The APS will question the appropriateness of traditional confrontational approaches as well as the effectiveness of the currently popular Motivational Interviewing[2] approach. Readers will be asked to consider a paradox that appears in the addiction counseling world: addiction counseling professionals who profess to embrace the reality of addictive disease also endorse an approach (M.I.) that does **not** consider addictive disease as a valid concept and in fact considers the core identifying feature of addiction, the loss of control (LoC) phenomena, to be a myth.

What exactly is goal of the APS?

The APS is an addiction-specific counseling strategy that relies upon the basic counseling skills of accurate empathy coupled with a sophisticated understanding of the LoC experience. The APS uses strategies that help the substance user examine their behavior and values to determine if they have crossed the line into addiction. In many ways, the APS is as much a philosophical approach to counseling as it is a set of specific counseling strategies. The primary philosophical position is that of highly valuing the client's subjective experience and interpretation of their world. This phenomenological orientation results in the counselor's helping the client examine their behavior within their own world-view and not against some external criteria. Motivation is developed as a result of the client's recognition of discrepancies between their behavior and their value system. The APS demonstrates practical strategies that can result in the addicted client acquiring intrinsic motivation to pursue an abstinence-based lifestyle. The APS gives the counselor a means to help the client build a strong foundation for recovery, a foundation built upon enlightened self-interest, not coercion. Given most clients who present for substance abuse issues are there as a result of some extrinsic motivator (judge, spouse, employer, etc), it is vital to avoid strategies that are based on power differentials or any type of confrontation because clients will tend to respond with compliance to this pressure, driving meaningful communication underground. The primary goal of the APS is to help the individual who is addicted to develop a significant level of intrinsic motivation to pursue recovery; counselors who align themselves with the extrinsic motivators greatly reduce their effectiveness to help the client.

Once the intrinsic motivation to pursue recovery has been awakened then a very difficult transition will occur that requires the counselor to use a different set of skills and approaches. Description and exploration of those skills is not the intent of this work and will not be included in this text except to note the common occurrence that recovering addicts report: they feel worse as they get better. Addicts who move into acceptance of their disease often experience despair, disorientation and confusion. It's as if they have been in a dark room and suddenly a bright light is turned on; it takes awhile to adjust to the light and to explore this once familiar room with the benefit of greater vision. The APS helps facilitate the destabilization of the structure that supported their addictive behavior; other approaches need to be used to help the person reconstitute themselves in their recovery.

The Anchor Point System can be adapted to almost any counseling situation where increasing consciousness regarding addictive disease is considered appropriate. Although the APS is fairly focused in its emphasis on exploring substance-use concerns, the counselor must have a "light grip" on this focus and prioritize the development of a trust-based relationship. Trust is built by being able to accurately reflect to the client the content, feelings and meanings of their communications. The counselor must remain responsive and willing to honor the client's process, which is rarely linear and is commonly filled with ambivalence. The APS requires patience! Although the APS can often be used very productively in a short period of time (1 to 3 counseling sessions), each client's unique presentation will dictate the speed at which the APS can be applied.

The APS is simple in its intent: to help clients with a substance-use concern accurately identify and articulate their beliefs about their relationship with that substance or substances. The interview is designed to emphasize and examine evidence of LoC. The APS involves specific techniques that were developed to help counselors facilitate a client's movements toward development of intrinsic motivation to address their substance-use concerns. This interview system is compatible with the needs of counselors who must produce documentation utilizing the DSM IV R criteria.

Why write this book now?

A war is being waged against addicts and against treatment for addiction across this country. While the casualties of this war are quietly growing in number, the carnage is very real. Untreated addiction costs lives, destroys families and exponentially grows misery. William White, the author of *Slaying the Dragon: The History of Addiction Treatment and Recovery in America*, predicted that in the new millennium "addiction will be de-medicalized and increasingly criminalized for all but the most affluent of our citizens." [3] He supports his vision of the future with the observation that "As we approach the 21st century, we have begun the wholesale movement of addicts-particularly poor addicts of color-from treatment programs to the criminal justice system." [4] He describes the underlying dynamic this way, " ...America is caught in a transition between two addiction paradigms: one that views addiction as a diseased condition emanating from biopsychosocial vulnerability, and the other that views addiction as willful and criminal behavior emanating from flaws of personal character." [5] Across the country, treatment centers are shutting their doors. Those on waiting lists to enter publicly funded facilities can wait months for a placement to open. The treatment centers that remain are increasingly pressured to align with economic forces that shorten stays and emphasize co-morbid diagnoses to maximize benefits. Addiction is increasingly relegated to a secondary concern as counseling staffs are more and more weighted with mental health professionals who have little training or direct experience with addiction. Counselors, recovering from addiction themselves, once the mainstay of treatment centers, have become a diminishing, and at times, an even absent influence.

William White's commentary on the differing contributions of the recovering and non-recovering counselors eloquently captures the cost of the recovering counselors demise.

> *"The noted mythologist Joseph Campbell often made distinctions between the roles of priests and shaman across different cultures. According to Campbell, priests were social functionaries who derived their legitimacy from social institutions and in turn supported the social order. In contrast, the shaman's legitimacy sprang from his or her passage through*

emotional death and rebirth. Where the priest had been prepared by the social order, the shaman was prepared by his or her own personal experience.6 "Professionals by education" and "professionals by experience" represent the priests and shaman of the addiction treatment field. For more than 100 years, tension has reigned in the relationship between our field's priest and shaman. That tension stems, in part, from two very different types of knowledge: the knowing of the mind and the knowing of the heart. The former involves the mastery of externally validated truth, while the latter springs from within one's own experiential truth."[7]

White, laments the loss of the presence of the recovering counselor.

"...we have lost, silenced, or transformed most of our shaman...Recovered and recovering people brought passion and energy to the treatment milieu. They brought a focus on direct service and a deep faith in the possibility of change derived from their own recovery and their participation in a community of recovered and recovering people. In the wake of their declining numbers, the presence of that hope in the field seems to be diminishing."[8]

What has accompanied the loss of the recovering counselor has been an erosion of an experienced-based understanding of addiction. More and more, trainings are provided by academics (priests) that are lacking actual experience of working with addiction. It has become increasingly difficult to attend an addiction specific training that is specific to addiction. The presence of PhD's (who are only rarely recovering or directly experienced with addiction) dominates the training terrain.

This book was written at this time to bring back to the addiction-counseling landscape the shaman's voice of experience. The pendulum has swung too far; we have moved from an over dependence on experience to an over-dependence on education devoid of real world experience. We need both the shaman and the priest to best serve addicts.

The ideal situation to best serve the addicted client is a staff balanced with both priestly and shamanic influences. A staff with no priest input is much more likely to miss important issues and obstacles, and it is more likely to operate from a "one size fits all" perspective. A staff with no shaman input is more likely to lose sight of the addiction and be seduced by issues other than those directly related to the addiction.

What is the current relationship between priest and shaman on the addiction counseling terrain?

The cooperation between priest and shaman has been an important contributor to the evolution of the addiction counseling profession. Consider the relationship between Dr. Harry Tiebout (priest), the psychiatrist who played an important role in the development of Alcoholic Anonymous, and Bill Wilson (shaman), one of the co-founders of AA. Tiebout was instrumental in opening doors so Wilson could make presentations at a New York state medical society meeting and later at a meeting of the

American Psychiatric Association. Bill Wilson's presentation was published in the American Journal of Psychiatry. Tiebout opened the professional doors through which A.A.'s legitimacy was acknowledged by medical and psychiatric authorities.[9] Without Tiebout, or another priest advocate, the doors would have remained closed.

A valid criticism has been waged against the over-valuing of shaman in the treatment community. There was certainly a time when recovery alone was considered sufficient criteria to use to hire someone to act as a 'professional' counselor. The section titled "Part One: Foundations" describes in detail how over-valuing of experience can result in ineffective and even harmful counseling practices. It is important to note that, at least in part, the over-valuing of experience occurred because of the lack of the availability of academic institutions that could prepare professionals to serve as addiction specific counselors.

Today, many of the priests who operate at the publishing level, seem to shun and discount the experience of the shaman. Consider the following three examples:

1) A recent text, *Alternatives to Abstinence* written by Heather Ogilvie, is based upon the following expertise:

> *"Until my publisher approached me about writing a book on alternative treatments for alcoholism, I had neither any special expertise in the subject nor any personal experience with alcohol problems."*[10]

2) Consider the often cited and quoted Herbert Fingarette (who has served as the United States representative on addictions to the United Nations) in his book *Heavy Drinking: The Myth of Alcoholism as a Disease* he claims that the reason he is an expert in the fields of addiction is because he has never done any actual research or worked with any actual addicts: thus he is an unbiased observer.[11]

3) The reigning high priests in the addiction community are William Miller and Stephen Rollnick, the authors of *Motivational Interviewing* (MI).[12] Their work has been heartily embraced by addiction counselors and remains one of the most popular trainings to attend in multitrack conferences. Most of the text is very helpful to the addiction counselor and surely contributes to the advancement of the evolution of the addiction counseling technology. However, Motivational Interviewing also contributes to the demise of the addiction paradigm that views addiction as a disease and contributes to the paradigm that "views addiction as willful and criminal behavior emanating from flaws of personal character." [13]

A core concept embraced by most shamans in the addiction counseling community is that "loss of control" (LoC) is the central identifying feature of addiction. LoC is defined as using a substance more than intended and using despite negative consequences. Recovering counselors tend to describe LoC in Alcoholics Anonymous terms: "We admitted we were powerless over alcohol—-that our lives had become unmanageable." Today's priest seems very certain that LoC is a myth. In the case of the

M.I. text, the only reference that the authors make to LoC is a parenthetical one:

> "That is, experiences and behaviors that follow ordinary principles of psychology are mistakenly interpreted as special symptoms indicative of unique addictive pathology (e.g., denial, craving, loss of control). "[14]

Thus it appears that many of today's priests not only discount the experience that shamans bring but challenge the most fundamental tenet the shamans hold: that they were powerless over their addiction.

Are the priests right? Is LoC a myth?

The contention that LoC is a myth seems to have wide support. In November 2001, during a meeting of the Oregon Consortium of Addiction Studies Educators one of the attendees proclaimed, "loss of control is a myth." The attendees served primarily as department chairs and/or as faculty members in colleges throughout Oregon. Their belief system is certainly reinforced across the curricula at their institutions, curricula that provides education for a large percentage of counselors entering the addiction-counseling field in this state. Only one voice opposed the view that LoC is a myth. Even William White in *Slaying the Dragon* seems to support this belief:

> *"The concepts of craving (cellular hunger for alcohol) and loss of control (the inability to limit the amount of alcohol consumed once drinking started)*

> *were similarly challenged in studies that failed to validate either the clear existence or the universality of these phenomena in alcoholics. Even the belief that the only option for alcoholics was complete abstinence from all alcohol was challenged in a series of studies revealing that a least a small percentage of alcoholics eventually achieved a state of sustained non-problematic drinking."*[15]

There does appear to be a number of studies that document the failure to produce in the laboratory the LoC experience. These studies, involving double blind procedures, examined the ability of alcohol to trigger a LoC reaction when a subject was given alcohol to consume (with or without their knowledge). LoC was not triggered in this setting. Let's assume that these studies are solid and sound in their methodology, analysis and conclusions. Is it sound scientific reasoning to conclude that, based upon the inability to create evidence of LoC in a laboratory setting, that LoC is a myth?

Imagine a series of studies designed to examine the question, "does God exist?" Now imagine that these studies failed to produce affirmative evidence for God's existence. It would be ludicrous to use these experiments as proof that God is a myth. Scientifically speaking, the only conclusion that could be reached is that these experiments failed to produce evidence that support the hypothesis that God exists. Similarly, the failure to replicate LoC in the laboratory setting doesn't *prove* anything, including the existence or non-existence of the LoC phenomenon. *Failure to provide* evidence is not equivalent to proving non-existence. The arrogant and illogical attachment to the belief that anything knowable is knowable only through available science is called scientism by Bruce Wilshire, the author of *Wild Hunger*. Scientism is a quasi-religious perspective that holds that all meaningful questions and answers are dependent upon science as the only reliable source of inquiry.[16] Lack of scientific understanding, or lack of technology that can measure or interact with a given phenomena, is used within scientism as proof for the affirmative. This type of application of science is a corruption used to press dogma, not further truth.

Consider the scientism in the following analysis provided by the author of *Alternatives to Abstinence*:

> *"The above experiments (and numerous others) refute the idea that once an alcoholic takes a drink he will inevitably lose control over how much he consumes. This led one disease proponent to redefine what was meant by loss of control in this way: If an alcoholic has a drink, he can never be sure that he will be able to stop. Loss of control is thus seen as something intermittent and unpredictable. This definition defies scientific testing, as it has been impossible to identify the conditions under which loss of control will occur and those under which it will not occur."*[17]

Is it logical to jump to the conclusion that LoC is non-existent simply because it appears to defy scientific testing or is currently elusive with available technology? Yet this is the dogma so many addiction-counseling priests are preaching. The silence created by the lack of shamanic voices cannot dismiss one truth: the voices of recovering addicts themselves.

To state that LoC is a myth is to discount the stated experience of countless recovering addicts who have articulated their experience with LoC in the form "We admitted we were powerless over alcohol that our lives had become unmanageable." It is an arrogant and grandiose position to dismiss the reality as described by these recovering people unless there is evidence to the contrary. Scientism is dogma, not evidence. During the last 15 years of work with physicians in recovery (over 90% of my private practice clients are male physicians), I have seen again and again these physicians embrace their addiction through identification of their LoC and acceptance of their "powerlessness." As physicians, these men are highly intelligent and strong willed and are trained to look at problems scientifically. They have gone to great lengths to control their use. If this group of men cannot learn to control their using, then who can? If this group of men is willing to claim their truth as involving being powerless over their addiction, on what basis can a distant laboratory endeavor be used to dismiss their experience and beliefs?

The addiction-counseling priests have been dismantling the disease paradigm and replacing it with the moral model supported by the scientism, which illogically dismisses LoC.

Is there contempt between the priest and the shaman?

White directly addressed this question:

> *"Contempt, often mutual, is an enduring and troubling theme in the historical relationship between helping professionals and addicts. The addiction treatment industry as a specialized field grew out of the contempt in which other helping systems regarded alcoholics and addicts. For generations, physicians, nurses, social workers, psychologists, welfare workers, and other service professionals barely masked their contempt for the alcoholic and addict. Beneath the veneer of professional discourse about addicts during the past century lie a pervasive undertone; most professionals simply do not like alcoholics and addicts."*[18]

Many shamans are suspicious of priests because of their historical relationship with professionals who have treated them with disdain. Imagine how the historical devaluing of shamans could currently magnify their distrust of the increasing presence of the priests. Priests, who hold the position that LoC is a myth, fuel this perception of contempt. When the experience of the shamans and the recognition of personal powerlessness is acknowledged, then the priests and the shamans can coexist in a mutually supportive and professionally efficient partnership to serve the clients.

A writer who represents the shaman's voice and provides an excellent analysis of the forces and dynamics fueling the anti-disease stance is James R. Milam. Milam describes two different paradigms in which one could attempt to understand addiction, the psychogenic and the biogenic. He describes the psychogenic model as being based "on the nearly universal belief that alcoholism is a symptom or consequence of an underlying character defect, a destructive response to psychological and social problems, a learned behavior." On the other hand, "biogenic model recognizes that alcoholism is a primary addictive response to alcohol in a biologically susceptible drinker, regardless of character and personality." Milam, who stands as a champion of the biogenic model, explains why Fingerette, the previously cited 'addiction-is-not-a-disease' philosopher, is able to claim that alcoholism is a myth: there is no evidence to support the psychogenic model! Fingarette's flaw then is not his research but his refusal to consider the alternative model of addiction, the biogenic model. There is an enormous and growing body of data that supports the biogenic model; genetic studies and neurochemistry advances probably proved the most compelling evidence to support this model. I would recommend highly that the reader consult Milam's work for a full exposure to his analysis.[19]

How does this work address LoC?

This book is intended for those who value the shaman's voice and the experience reflected in that voice. The addiction counseling field is in desperate need of becoming reacquainted with the core characteristic of addiction: LoC. To understand addiction is to understand the conflict the addict experiences as they engage in behaviors (using) that conflict with their values. LoC is the cause of this conflict and is essential to understand if one wishes to truly be able to be compassionate and responsive to the suffering addict.

If you believe that addiction is a secondary disorder to some "core issue", this book is not for you. If you believe that controlled using is a realistic goal for an addict, this book is not for you. If you understand that the single most important core issue to address if one intends to help an addicted individual is the LoC experience, then welcome and thank you for being willing to consider the APS.

An invitation to priest and shaman

In closing this introduction, I invite the priest to examine this material as a means to becoming better priest. Priests who value shamans understand it is the balance between the two that will best serve clients. Shamans, stand firm in the conviction of your experience but be open to reconsidering how you have interpreted and applied that experience to your clients. Shamans who value priests understand the importance of bringing all available resources to the aid of the addict who still suffers. We need priest and shamans who stand in mutual support of each other if we wish to best help the addicts who seek our help.

A brief note on language, to honor both men and women, I have chosen to alternate the use of the male and female pronouns throughout this work.

For any reader, priest or shaman, who would like to give feedback to the author, know that your feedback would be greatly appreciated.

Jon Gieber MS CADC II
24205 NE Alvas Rd
Battle Ground, WA 98604
United States of America
December, 2002

KEY CONCEPTS

Anchor Point System (APS): The addiction specific counseling strategy described in this book.

Loss of Control (LoC): The core identifying feature of addiction. Defined as using a substance more than intended and/or using despite negative consequences.

Priest: Addiction counseling professionals whose expertise is a result of education.

Scientism: A quasi-religious perspective where anything not knowable through science (or current technology) is viewed as non-existent.

Phenomenological: Focus on the subjective experience of the other.

Shaman: Addiction counseling professionals whose expertise is a result of personal experience.

Sources

1) *Twelve Steps and Twelve Traditions.* (1953) Alcoholics Anonymous World Services, Inc. New York, New York. pg. 5

2) Miller, William R and Rollnick, Stephen (1991). *Motivational Interviewing: Preparing People to Change Addictive Behavior.* New York, New York: Guilford Press.

3) White, William (1998). *Slaying the Dragon: The History of Addiction Treatment and Recovery in America.* Bloomington, Illinois: Chestnut Health Systems/Lighthouse Institute, pg. 341

4) White, pg. 341

5) White, pg. 341

6) White, pg. 336, 337. Reference to Campbell, J. with Bill Moyers (1988) *The Power of Myth.* New York: Anchor Books. pg. 73

7) White, pg. 337

8) White, pg. 337

9) White, pg. 142

10) Ogilvie, Heather (2001). *Alternative to Abstinence: A New Look at Alcoholism and the Choices in Treatment.* Long Island City, New York: Hatherleigh Press. pg xix

11) Fingarette, Herbert (1988). *Heavy Drinking.* Berkeley, California: The University of California Press. 1988

12) Miller and Rollnick

13) White, pg. 341

14) Miller, pg 11

15) White, 288

16) Wilshire, Bruce (1999). *Wild Hunger: the primal roots of modern addiction.* Cumnor Hill, Oxford, England: Rowman & Littlefield Publishers, Inc. pg 40, 41

17) Ogilvie, pg 67

18) White, pg 332

19) Milam, James R. *The Alcoholism Revolution*, Professional Counselor, August 1992.

Chapter 1: Foundations

The intent of this chapter is to give an overview of the experiences and beliefs that resulted in the creation of the counseling approach known as the Anchor Point System. While this chapter is autobiographical in nature, I have been able to validate the accuracy of the general themes and concepts through my 20+ years of work with recovering addicts and counselors who have either been in or worked in a large variety of institutions throughout the Pacific Northwest.

Slaying the Dragon

November 1979. Deep in the heart of my raging cocaine addiction, a blessing of clear perception came upon me early one Sunday morning. I had spent the night with a friend holed up in a hotel room using cocaine. Earlier that Saturday, the friend had called to tell me he was afraid; he had stolen drugs from some dealers and now had a considerable amount of cocaine in his possession. It had taken nothing more than his saying he would share his cocaine with me for me to agree to keep him company. I had no regard for my safety (if the dealers found him, the danger would have been quite real), and I placed my girlfriend in jeopardy as well. The night was filled with cocaine and paranoid delusions; in fact severe paranoia had already become my constant companion. I spent hours that night staring out a crack in the curtain and listening to the walls for the sound of approaching feet. When I arrived home at 9:00 the next morning, I noticed three men in a nearby field with surveying equipment. In my delusional state, these men became killers with shotguns who were going to assassinate me. With too little sleep and too much cocaine in my system, I forced myself to try to sleep. Lying on my bed, I again stared out the crack in the curtains, as I knew the assassins would eventually circle my house as they tried to locate me. In this moment, I found myself watching myself watching for assassins. I saw how bizarre my thinking had become; I saw clearly the precipice upon which I stood. In this moment, I saw a fork in the road: one path led to oblivion of any remaining facets of my true self, to total corruption of my soul. The other path was equally frightening; to abandon the world I knew and try to find out what had become of me. The first path seemed to guarantee oblivion, while the second contained a shred of hope, of redemption amidst the uncertainty. In this moment, I knew deep in my bones, that continued use of drugs would inevitably kill my very essence. This moment was pivotal, and I was never to be the same. To this day, I feel blessed that this moment of clarity was given to me and humbled by my certainty of what would have happened to me without this gift.

The clarity I received was not by itself enough. Too many times already I had briefly awakened only to fall back to sleep to the nightmare that was my addicted life. I was certain that I would continue to use if I did not reach outside of myself and get help. It became obvious to me that I must start telling the truth and recruit others to help me. This clear perception led me to a revealing session with my parents. They gave witness to my truth by listening, they gave me hope by acting, and they showed wisdom by recognizing that while they could love me, others needed to help me. After a few days of considering other options, I saw clearly that if I wished to stay clean, I needed a treatment facility. Anything less than a residential facility left me certain that I would soon use again. When I entered that facility, I got more than I could have imagined, not only my recovery but also the beginning to my addiction-counseling career.

In order to recover, I had to reconstruct myself. My belief systems in particular needed to be deconstructed and then reassembled. I needed to unlearn certain ideas and learn new ones. Before I describe the truths I learned while in that facility, the truths that changed my life and formed the foundation of my counseling career, it is important to digress and briefly discuss the various sources for truth one can draw upon.

Essential Truths

I believe that identifying the source of one's truth is vital to the ethical application and attachment to any given truth. Equally important is the ability to recognize if a truth is applicable to others or relevant only for a certain individual. This is especially important when working within the addiction-counseling arena where power differentials between counselor and client are the norm not the exception. Counselors could impose their truth upon a client, in effect forcing the client to adopt a given truth (or at least appear to adopt the truth) or face the consequences that arise from the power differential. The importance of being aware of power differentials will be discussed in greater depth later in this manual.

Truth arises from five basic sources: authority, experience, intuition, science and legal process. I will now define each type of truth, give an example of this truth and then briefly describe how application of this type of truth is commonly used in the addiction treatment world before returning to the truths I learned while in treatment for my own addiction.

Authority

Truth can be obtained by accepting that which comes from an authority figure as truth. The authority position may be granted, as is the case of one who chooses to follow a particular religious organization and adhere to that religion's truths, or could be imposed, as is the case of an employee who must choose to adhere to the truth of an employer as a condition of continued employment. This truth is not arguable. This type of truth is simply a declared truth that hinges entirely upon one's belief in the right of the authority to lay claim to the declaration of truth. One can accept or reject the authority's right to declare the truth, but to argue the truth itself is very non-productive.

Example: Several years ago I was asked to participate in a debate. The question to be debated was "Is addiction a disease?" I was very thorough preparing my arguments and supporting evidence and felt very confident as I proceeded to the debate. I had failed to take into account that

I was debating a minister who claimed the authority to declare that addiction was the result of sin. His position was not arguable for he had no evidence, no science, no developed reasoning. What he had was the simple inarguable declaration that addiction is a sin. For him, this was an article of faith that simply was not open to scrutiny.

Application: It is common for counselors in treatment facilities to adopt an authority position and require their clients to accept their pronouncements. Failure to accept this authority is usually cited as evidence that the individual has not accepted their powerlessness and is therefore not in recovery. This practice is so common I have created a term, Post Traumatic Treatment Disorder (to be fully explained later), to describe the lasting effect that having truth imposed from an authority position coupled with a significant power differential can cause. Many clients end up in treatment because they are 'willing' to acquiesce to a perceived authority's truth (see legal truth).

Experience

Truth can be obtained through personal experience. This type of truth is very powerful and is the most significant type of truth in terms of inclusion into an individual's psyche. The individual who acquires truth via personal experience is prone to believing that this truth is applicable to others.

Example: Alcoholics Anonymous appears to understand the significant difference between telling someone what they ought to believe (authority based truth) and helping someone use their own experience to ferret out what they actually believe. A commonly used concept in Alcoholics Anonymous is that it is not useful to tell someone what to do, but rather one should share his or her "experience, strength and hope." Meeting attendees are encouraged to "take what they can use and leave the rest."

Application: Treatment facilities have relied heavily upon individuals who have direct experience with addiction. Truth obtained from personal experience is usually the single greatest contributor to the treatment practice of counselors. Treatment counselors who are recovering individuals are likely to re-enact the behaviours they experienced as clients. Non-recovering personnel are very prone to emulate the more senior Counselor's clinical repertoire and philosophy.

Truth based upon experience can be very helpful for the addiction Counselor. It can also be very limiting and self-serving. Truth based on experience needs to be balanced by intuition and science.

Intuition

Truth can be obtained by awareness experienced via dreams, feelings or other body based sensations. This type of truth is not based on external factors but rather on unseen forces that are not readily measurable or observable.

Example: My wife, Janey Gieber, is a cancer survivor. She survived because of her intuitive ability. Without a single shred of physical evidence, with a minimal history of cancer in her family, and despite her physician's dismissal of her concerns, at the age of 37 she simply knew she had cancer. She trusted her intuition and forced her physician to conduct screening tests to address her concerns. Her action saved her life, as her intuition was correct and allowed her to receive the treatment she needed.

Application: Intuition is a vital component to almost any counseling process. The counselor's ability to use their own internal world to help guide their ability to be responsive and helpful to their client is a hallmark of an advanced counselor. Conversely, overvaluing intuition by turning hunches into facts can be very dangerous. Many clients in addiction facilities have been bludgeoned with a counselor's hunch-turned-fact ranting concerning how the counselor knows that they are "in denial." Intuition needs to be tempered with truth that arises from experience and science.

Science

Truth can be obtained through the use of the scientific method. This truth is based upon the creation of a hypothesis that is testable by objective means. If evidence is gathered that supports the hypothesis, then it is scrutinized by others conducting similar types of research. Replication of the same research is needed if the hypothesis is to be stated with any certainty. The scientific method results in a probability assessment as to the confidence of any given hypothesis. The scientific method includes, by definition, a self-correcting feature that allows inclusion of new evidence and re-evaluation of previously accepted truths.

For the sake of completeness, I would add to this definition of a scientific truth any truth that is based upon a client's statements that appear to be based in reality and sound thinking. If a client tells me that they are addicted to nicotine, I would consider it safe to assume that they are indeed addicted to nicotine. If information contrary to the client's statements were to emerge then I would question the veracity of the information they produced. Similarly, one would hope that educational institutions deliver the most current science based content in their curricula.

Example: Individuals who appear in treatment as a result of their alcohol addiction and who are also addicted to nicotine have often been counselled not to address their nicotine addiction until after at least one year of being alcohol free. The working hypothesis is that it is destabilizing and counterproductive to address nicotine addiction simultaneously with other chemical addictions. Research has not confirmed this belief. One study evaluated the progress of residents in an alcoholism treatment facility undergoing a standard nicotine cessation program compared to a group of smoking alcoholics in the same facility that did not undergo the smoking cessation program. One year after treatment, the results indicated that the smoking cessation program had no effect on abstinence from alcohol or other drugs, but that 12% of the subjects who went through smoking cessation treatment had quit smoking while no member of the other group had quit smoking. (From alert #39 NIAAA)

Application: One would think that science is essential to counseling the addicted population. Science appears to be used heavily but is usually prioritised behind experience and authority as the predominant sources of truth in treatment. Science is often used in lectures and discussion surrounding addictive disease but is less commonly used as a source for extracting clinical approaches and philosophies. A trend that I will speak to at great length in this manual involves the perversion of science in such a way that the essential identifying characteristic of addiction, the loss of control experience, is claimed to be a myth.

Legal Process

Truth can be obtained through the use of legal argument. While similar to truth based on authority, this type of truth is more process and precedent driven. One is subject to legal truth when they decide to live in a particular area and give an implicit agreement to abide by the laws and legal process of that area.

Example: Each state has a board that governs the behaviour of physicians who are licensed in that state. Many states have programs that facilitate the identification, treatment and monitoring of physicians who are believed to be addicted. Physicians may have their licenses revoked if they do not comply with the treatment and monitoring requirements of that state. Once a physician is referred to a given treatment facility, then that facility has an enormous amount of power over that physician. Failure to comply with the treatment facility is usually viewed as synonymous with failure to comply with the licensing board. Obviously, the power differential in this situation is immense.

Application: Clients who arrive in treatment as a result of a legal truth make up a significant amount of most counselor's caseload. It can be very difficult for counselors to be able to honor the extrinsic motivation that brought the client to treatment while not aligning with that source of motivation. Failure to remain separate from this extrinsic motivator usually irreparably damages the counseling relationship. How to manage this dynamic will be discussed at length later in the manual.

In summary:

In order to be a professional and ethical counselor one must determine the source of the truth upon which they build their counseling philosophy and clinical approach. There are five main sources of truth: authority, experience, intuition, science and legal process. Once the counselor is conscious of the type of truth they employ then they must be very thoughtful in how they apply that truth to any given counseling situation.I will now return to the truth I learned while in treatment for my own addiction.

The New Paradigm

The old way of thinking I needed to relinquish in order to move into recovery was fairly simple. While I do not intend to dishonor the complexities and subtleties of the human psyche (especially mine!) by being to simplistic, I learned in treatment that there were three basic beliefs that needed to be challenged in order to move into recovery. While individuals certainly brought many other issues and beliefs to the table, these three beliefs seemed to be the universal core shared by all the addicts in the facility. The three beliefs:

1) I could control my using.
2) I simply need to be stronger.
3) I don't need help.

While in treatment I learned that these beliefs were the prison bars that kept my true freedom captive and my addiction active. In order to emancipate myself from addiction I needed to deconstruct this internal prison by tearing down these bars of belief. My freedom needed to be built upon a new foundation. The cornerstones of this new foundation required that I internalize three new beliefs:

A) Addiction is a disease.
B) Addicts have highly developed denial systems.
C) Denial must be confronted.

Addiction is a disease

The former belief that "I could control my using" lay in shards as I examined the history of my using. Multiple attempts at controlling my using had failed. While it was possible for periods of time to lessen my using, a big picture vantage point showed that eventually, without fail, my use always became greater than I had intended and I ended up paying a price I didn't really want to pay. I came to understand that the Alcoholics Anonymous first step, "We admitted we were powerless over alcohol that our lives had become unmanageable," captured the essence of the addictive disease. My belief that "I simply need to be stronger" succumbed to an understanding that it didn't matter how bright, or moral, or actualized I was, that if I used a mood-altering chemical, then I was at significant risk that I would eventually use more than I intended and pay a price I didn't want to pay. I couldn't unlearn, out think or grow out of addiction. I was taught that addiction is a disease that is activated by use and that if can be kept in remission by abstinence. No matter how long one is abstinent, if they choose to use again, they do so with a significant risk of activating their disease and losing the ability to predict when they will start or stop using. The paradox of recovery became readily apparent to me, instead of believing that "I simply need to be stronger," by accepting that I am powerless over my addiction, I can gain back all of my personal power. Accepting one's powerlessness then is not a victim stance but an act of personal empowerment. My freedom from addiction is based upon my internalization of the understanding that addiction is indeed a disease, a disease that causes LoC to happen over time, not every time.

Addicts have highly developed denial systems

While in treatment I also learned that denial is so common that clients are taught not to trust their own thinking and judgment. The unpredictable nature of LoC facilitated the denial response because the addict focuses on the few times he or she would control their using instead of the many times they would experience LoC. Prior to my moment of clarity, I rarely allowed myself to consider the possibility that my using was problematic. At one point I had even assisted my father's entry into treatment for his alcoholism, attended many counseling sessions with him during the day and then returned home at night to sell and use drugs. While in treatment I became aware that I had betrayed myself in many important ways to allow my use to continue. The lies I told myself were numerous and extensive. My interaction with other clients in treatment confirmed the counselor's portrayal of denial as an essential component of the addictive experience. Learning to become honest and work through the layers of denial is fundamental to recovery and is a process that may take several months, if not years, to accomplish.

Denial must be confronted

Denial was the major obstacle to acceptance of my addiction. The primary mode of treatment I received was group therapy, and there we confronted the various modes of denial we used. The group included family involvement where the counselor facilitated the family's expression of their pain and trauma associated with the addict's using. Group therapy emphasized the identification and expression of feelings and encouraged the clients to give each other feedback. Group members became very adept at using the confrontational and feedback techniques with each other. Older group members often led the charge in giving feedback to newer group members. Confrontation was the primary mode of intervention in addressing denial, and the primary job of the counselor in treatment was helping clients face their denial and accept their powerlessness.

The Blind Leading the Blind

Armed with the truth I learned about recovery, and relying on my own experience as a recovering addict, I decided to pursue a career in addiction counseling. While I greatly valued the knowledge my experience had taught me about addiction, I knew that it was not enough. After a year of recovery, I returned to the University of Oregon to finish my Bachelor of Science in Psychology. After I finished my degree in 1981 I wanted to help others who struggled with addictive disease; however, my psychology degree did not contribute in any meaningful way to my becoming an addiction counselor. The only important information I left the university with concerning addiction was that there didn't seem to be much interest in it, and as I looked at the other Oregon schools, I was shocked to realize that there were no addiction-specific training programs available. How was I to learn how to be an addiction counselor if there was no one to teach me?

As I turned away from academia for addiction-specific training, I turned to addiction-specific counselors to unravel the secret of how they became professional counselors. I was quite surprised to learn that most people had become addiction counselors by default. The profession was so new that in Oregon in the late 70's, an organization called The New Professionals had been formed for addiction-specific counselors. This organization hoped to move addiction counselors from the status of para-professional to full fledged professional. I realized that addiction treatment was still struggling to establish itself as a legitimate endeavor. There simply did not exist a significant body of qualified knowledgeable addiction professionals to tap into for treatment centers to meet their hiring needs. In order to staff their facilities, they hired the most competent person they could find without being burdened by a minimum standard of professional preparation. During this era, it wasn't unusual for someone who was a client in a facility one day to be an employed staff person the next. Many, if not most of the counselors, during this time were recovering individuals who were somehow deemed appropriate, hired and given a caseload. Those non-recovering counselors typically had a Master's degree in counseling or social work; while they were usually knowledgeable about counseling, they knew very little about addiction from their formal education. Both the recovering and non-recovering counselors were learning addiction counseling as they did it!

The lack of any addiction-specific training program in Oregon led me to create my own training opportunity by volunteering on Saturdays at a treatment facility. Through this volunteer position, I hoped to observe and learn from experienced addiction counselors. The first Saturday I sat in with a staff member, but then I was on my own for the next 6 months, I was the sole "counselor" on duty. Using meager guidelines, I counseled by the seat of my pants and I began to think that I knew something about being an addiction counselor. This illusion was further reinforced when six months later I landed a job as a full time case manager in another residential treatment facility. I now had to maintain the illusion of my competency and then allow myself to forget that it was an illusion at all. My employer, my clients, my colleagues all seemed to want me to be confident in my abilities so I quickly blinded myself to doubt and became very efficient at "breaking denial."

As my skills as a sledgehammer, denial-busting surgeon were becoming well honed, my new boss affirmed my role. One day he told me, *"You'll know you're doing your job if you're walking down the hall to do Group, and one group member sees you approaching and turns to the another and says, 'Here comes that son of a bitch now'."* Thus, confrontation was clearly encouraged, and it became the main tool of my limited arsenal of clinical behaviors. My creativity flourished in the vacuum of autonomy that was my daily reality. At this point in my career, I had never had a single minute of supervision! While there were certainly meetings about making appropriate chart notes and paper trails, the greatest attention was spent on issues regarding census and making call-back contacts to prospective clients. There was no time spent observing Group, discussing appropriate clinical interventions for different situations, or wondering about issues of countertransferance.

Eventually, buoyed by others' confidence in me, I took a position with greater responsibilities at another facility. Empowered with a larger caseload and greater responsibility, my creative juices flowed. Confrontational tactics involving mock funerals (including obituaries), declaring "bull shit" loudly in Group when my gut sniffed out "denial," power staffings (where a client would be confronted by the entire clinical staff), and other emotionally brutal approaches predominated. All of this behavior was based on one simple belief: I knew what the truth was and the clients were in denial and needed to accept the truth in order to move into recovery. My truth, based upon my experience and intuition and further supported by the authority given me by the various referral sources trumped any truth offered by a client, and if clients did not comply with my truth they often had severe sanctions to face. The staff was mutually supportive and organized in our confrontational approach, which facilitated the client's acquisition of the truth. It was at this facility that my reign of terror reached its zenith.

A Single Match can Light the Darkness

While at the aforementioned facility, I had the good fortune to meet a psychologist, Dr. Janice Green, who helped open my eyes to my arrogance and brutality. The single most important thing that Dr. Green did was to ask me to get curious about what I thought I knew. She didn't give me answers but rather helped me understand that there were important questions to ask. As I began to examine what I did with clients and what evidence there was that I was being helpful, I rapidly became mortified. It was as if she woke me from a dream that I didn't know I was dreaming. I saw that I was one of the townspeople proclaiming how fine the emperor looked in his new clothes and didn't realize that he was actually naked; I had convinced myself he really had on some fine new clothes! My repetition of the behaviors I had learned while in treatment, my overvaluing of my intuition, my abuse of the power differential inherent with most of my clients, was suddenly revealed to me. I began to see the hideous nature of my own behavior. Who was I to declare what the truth was for someone else? How could I be so sure what was best for someone else? What evidence did I have that someone was in denial? Who gave me the magical ability to have a "gut" that could override the stated truth of another human being? My colleagues were less than enthusiastic with my new emerging, less certain, gentler, more client-empowering self. In fact, my boss was absolutely beside herself when I begin to question the very tactics I had previously employed on my clients. After several go-rounds with her, I was fired.

Now I was a young, increasingly self-aware, unemployed counselor. As fate would have it, I was hired at the same facility where I had been a patient several years earlier. This major treatment center had a very solid reputation. I was excited to have a chance to work in this facility and learn from the very best. Perhaps now I would get the training and the supervision I really needed. However, this was not to be the case.

I had a remaining illusion that the staff at this facility knew what they were doing. In reality, each of the five inpatient group facilitators ran Group as a reflection of their own personalities and experience. There was very limited supervision and no professional dialogue (What do you do in your group? How do you know if someone is in recovery? How do you select treatment approaches for different clients? What are the most important elements of the rehabilitative process when working with the addicts?). And, just as when I was a client in this facility, the core strategy of confrontation dominated the treatment practice.

At a professional crisis and no longer believing that I had any idea if I was harming or helping my clients, I decided to return to the University of Oregon and pursue a Master's in Counseling. While I understood that addiction was not considered a legitimate area of academic interest at the university, I believed that at least now I understood the importance of asking the right questions. My focus was to learn what scientific truths were available relevant to the understanding of addiction. Even though there were no professors at the university I could find who were interested in addiction, whenever possible I would use my class assignments, papers and projects as an opportunity to focus on addiction. This strategy allowed me to read the available research and draw my own conclusions.

It was at this time that I found a curious little study involving 66 state-funded treatment centers in New Jersey. This study asked one basic question: "What are the most important elements of the rehabilitative process?" The results concluded that there was virtually no agreement on what the most important elements were. Finally others, at least in New Jersey, had confirmed my own suspicion that flying by the seat of one's pants was the norm in addiction work, not the exception!

Subsequent research and inquiry further allowed me to become comfortable with my own ignorance. At least I knew that I didn't know and I no longer had to pretend that I knew. I was able to embrace my ignorance and replace the arrogance of certainty with healthy measures of humility, compassion and curiosity. Freed from the shackles of righteousness, I could begin to evolve as an addiction counselor. But who would hire me now? Who would want to hire someone who was now willing to "rock the boat" and question the prevailing treatment dogma? Someone who was willing to ask: "What evidence do you have that they are an addict? What is addiction? How do I know someone is in denial? What is recovery? How does a given counseling approach facilitate movement into recovery? What is relapse? Are the

12-step programs for everyone? Am I sure? How did I come to that conclusion?

Redemption

With a growing sense of comfort about what I didn't know and an understanding of how vital it is to question and probe the clinician's beliefs and behaviors, I found myself very unsure about finding a job. At this juncture, the Universe appeared to intervene with a wink, and out of the blue, a job announcement surfaced for a teaching position in a community college alcohol and drug counselor-training program. I decided that at least I knew I was ignorant and I had as much right to try and teach what I didn't know as anyone else! After a rigorous application and interview process, I was offered the position. I have been a full time instructor at Portland Community College in Portland, Oregon, since 1987.

Early in my teaching career, while conducting a seminar for more than 50 experienced group facilitators, I asked the audience, "How many counselors present feel like you make up Group as you go along and primarily fly by the seat of your pants?" Almost every person raised his or her hand. Further discussion revealed that their counselors were unclear about what to do as group facilitators and why they used the interventions they did in treatment settings. This confirmed for me the results from the New Jersey study, that there was virtually no agreement on what the most important elements of the rehabilitative process were.

This experience encouraged me to examine the basic question, "What, in the addiction-counselor profession, is the primary source of truth"? It became evident that the basis of clinical practice with addicts primarily involved truth derived from experience. Counselors relied on their own experience as a client or on their observation of someone else's work with clients, and they replicated these behaviors. This type of "training" was self-reinforcing, and it did not reflect any significant consideration of academic or scientific examination of these behaviors. Even if a counselor wanted to include an academic/scientific component to their training, it was very difficult to do so. Addiction seemed to be in most academic institutions, relegated to a secondary disorder, one not worthy of consideration as a primary issue. Addiction counselors were left to replicate what they saw other counselors do and to rely on their own intuition.

The treatment centers themselves did little to train addiction counselors; there seemed to be an unspoken understanding that once one was hired as a counselor, one knew how to be a counselor. Nor was there much in the way of supervision that involved examination of the counselor's role in treatment. Supervision consisted of examining the counselor's ability to complete the necessary paperwork in a timely fashion and to ensure compliance with the requirements of governing bodies. Supervision almost never occurred regarding what the counselor actually did with their clients.

So what did counselors do with their clients? No one really knew, except the counselors and their clients.

Group, the primary mode of treatment delivery, was a function of the individual counselor's autonomy, experience, and belief system. Counselors rarely discussed with each other what they did with clients; instead their discussion almost always focused on clients' behavior.

The counselors' clinical behaviors were assumed to be helpful and appropriate and were rarely questioned. However, while the counselor's clinical behavior was highly variable, there was a fairly unified and succinct belief system that flowed throughout the treatment world. This belief system and the language that expressed it allowed counselors to communicate with each other regarding client behaviors, and it provided a unifying fabric that allowed counselors to justify almost any behavior they employed in the name of treatment.

As a result of working from 1981 through 1992 in six treatment centers, maintaining a private practice since 1991 where I work with physicians who have been in treatment at a variety of facilities, and through serving as a practicum supervisor for many students affording me an opportunity to examine the fundamental beliefs of a large number of treatment facilities, I am very confident that the basic belief system I learned over twenty years ago is still the predominant belief system employed in the majority of treatment centers today. Given this belief system, the counselor's job then is to help the client through dismantling their denial system (as guided by their intuition) to facilitate recognition that they have a disease, which will require that they attend 12 step meetings if they hope to recover.

What then is the Truth?

This manual will examine the basic belief system outlined above and will propose that it be reconsidered. It will describe my current conclusions about what motivates addicts to change and how specific techniques can be used to facilitate the client's adoption of intrinsic motivation to pursue recovery. While not arrogant enough to proclaim that "I know the truth," I am very committed to describing my current best thinking as an invitation for you to consider yours. Evolution of thought cannot happen without examination of one's belief systems. While it certainly makes one vulnerable to expose their beliefs to the light of day (especially when done in writing), how else can one evolve their thinking? The truths that this work is based on will be outlined in detail in part two; until then consider asking: What truths do you base your interactions with addicts upon? How do you define addiction? What evidence do you have that this is an accurate definition? What criteria do you use to decide if a client is an addict? What is denial? How would you decide if a client is in denial? What is recovery? What criteria do you use to decide if a client is in recovery?

One truth, which I used to heartily embrace, was that confrontation is required to help clients interrupt their denial systems. This manual, which is a culmination of my efforts over the years to correct my earlier attachment to confrontation, is my best vehicle for making amends to the clients I may have harmed by using confrontational tactics that placed my "truth" above theirs. Finding a way to respectfully and humanely address the needs of a person struggling with the disease of addiction has become my primary professional goal.

I developed APS (Anchor Point System) because I could not find other counseling models that incorporate a realistic understanding of addictive disease with a researched-based respectful approach to counseling. While Motivational Interviewing is an excellent general counseling strategy, it does not honor, nor seem to even understand, the natural evolution of the addictive experience. The Anchor Point System is an addiction-specific strategy that is based on compassion, developed empathy and reflective listening skills. The APS requires that the counselor understand the addictive experience and be able to provide a guided and direct examination of the client's subjective world. Understanding the addictive experience is in a large part defined by understanding the expression of the LoC phenomena in each individual addict's life. While I do not contend that everyone who has a problematic relationship with mood-altering drugs is addicted, I strongly believe that anyone who is addicted will have already operationally defined LoC within their own experience. I consider the element of LoC to be so important that I have devoted a lengthy section entitled Dangerous Tides to articulate my concerns regarding the peril the addiction counseling profession is in as it has embraced Motivational Interviewing and neglected the core feature of addiction, LoC.

The intent of this work is to provide an approach that uses both the priest and the shaman perspective, science coupled with experience. We need to honor the contributions that both perspectives offer and synthesize the contributions that each has to make into a model that best serves addicts. This manual provides counselors a specific and defined approach to use when attempting to help someone explore their historic relationship with mood-altering drugs, and where appropriate, helping them identify the LoC that results in a conflict with their values. The APS is designed to honor each client's unique experience and not to burden him or her with preconceived ideas or plans of action. The current set of beliefs that are used to build the APS is the focus of the next chapter.

KEY CONCEPTS

I) Essential Truths

1. *Authority* - truth based upon position or assignment.
2. *Experience* - truth based upon personal experience.
3. *Intuition* - truth derived from an inner, immeasurable source.
4. *Science* - statement of probabilities derived from scientific inquiry.
5. *Legal Process* - truth derived from argument and/or precedent.

II) The New Paradigm

1. *Addiction is a disease.*
2. *Addicts have highly developed denial systems.*
3. *Denial must be confronted.*

III) Questions to Consider:

1. What source of truth(s) do you depend upon for your understanding of addiction?
2. What source of truth(s) do you depend upon for your understanding of counseling?
3. How sure are you about these truths?
4. After considering the truths described in *The New Paradigm*, condense your truths about recovery from addiction into a small number of definitive statements.

Chapter 2: The Shaman Priest

This chapter is devoted to synthesizing the truths learned from experience (shaman) with the truths learned through academic inquiry (priest) into a coherent foundation upon which to build APS. There is a need to be vigilant against the dogma of scientism, but also to be vigilant against the zealous application of personal experience as generalized truth. One antidote to dogma derived from either scientism or personal experience is to hold the philosophical position that evidence that contradicts experience should be valued simply as experience that contradicts evidence. The truth is relative and needs to be understood within the context of its source. There needs to be careful and thoughtful process before dismissing any type of truth, no matter what its source.

To summarize the truths learned from experience presented in the preceding chapter:

1) *Addiction is a disease.*
2) *Addicts have highly developed denial systems.*
3) *Denial must be confronted.*

Addiction is a disease

Definition of addiction

Shaman view: The prevailing shamanic belief is that addiction is a disease. This belief is perhaps best demonstrated by noting the attachment the shaman has to the concept of being "powerless" as described in the 12 step programs. The primary feature of addiction is described as the addict's inability to consistently predict what will happen once they consume mood-altering drugs. Being "powerless" is not described as a philosophical position but rather is a statement of fact that describes an individual's historical relationship with mood altering chemicals. The shaman's view does not emphasis the cause of the addiction, nor does it concern itself with arguments over the use of the word disease; instead it focuses on the individual's self assessment of their experience with being powerless over their addiction.

Priest view: The prevailing priestly belief is that addiction is not a disease. This view is espoused by some highly visible educators in the addiction-counseling world and by several published authors, especially Miller and Rollnick, authors of M.I. Their view, while widespread, does not appear to reflect the majority of addiction-specific professionals.

The prevailing medical view is that addiction is a disease. The National Institute of Drug Abuse, the single largest funding source for addiction related research in the world, publishes its findings in a variety of formats. One format is intended to be used as an educational tool to teach the basics of addiction. Included in the materials for this presentation is the unequivocal position of NIDA, "Scientist have learned a great deal about the biochemical, cellular and molecular base of addiction; it is clear that addiction is a disease of the brain."[1]

The American Society of Addiction Medicine supports this position:

"Alcoholism is a primary, chronic disease with genetic, psychosocial, and environmental factors influencing its development and manifestations. The disease is often progressive and fatal. It is characterized by continuous or periodic impaired control over drinking, preoccupation with the drug alcohol, use of alcohol despite adverse consequences, and distortions in thinking, most notably denial."

"Impaired control means the inability to limit alcohol use or to consistently limit on any drinking occasion the duration of the episode, the quantity consumed, and/or the behavioral consequences of drinking."

(Approved by ASAM Board of Directors February 25, 1990. The remainder of their public policy statement can be found at their website which is www.asam.org.)[2]

In a more recent position statement issued by the American Society of Addiction Medicine, the American Academy of Pain Medicine, and the American Pain Society (approved in February of 2001) the definition of alcoholism was broadened to be more encompassing of other drug use and to provide an important distinction between addiction and physical dependency:

"Addiction is a primary, chronic, neurobiological disease, with genetic, psychosocial, and environmental factors influencing its development and manifestations.

It is characterized by behaviors that include one or more of the following: impaired control over drug use, compulsive use, continued use despite harm, and craving."

"Physical Dependence is a state of adaptation that often includes tolerance and is manifested by a drug class specific withdrawal syndrome that can be produced by abrupt cessation, rapid dose reduction, decreasing blood level of the drug, and/or administration of an antagonist."[3]

Physical Dependency vs. Addiction

There are two significant reasons to clearly articulate the distinction between addiction and physical dependency: confusion between the two result in pain patients being under-treated and addicts who do not exhibit physical dependency being under-diagnosed.

Sidney H. Schnoll, M.D, Medical College of Virginia, directly addressed the under treatment issue for pain patients in a column posted at healthcentral.com[4]

"...If someone becomes physically dependent on a drug, that is not addiction. These two concepts - addiction and physical dependence should be clearly differentiated. It turns out that many people who physicians think are addicts - because they demand more medication and/or have persistent pain symptoms - are not necessarily addicts. They just need more medication for the treatment of their chronic pain. So it's a matter of recognizing that it is not addiction you are

treating but inadequate treatment of their pain. In other words, they are appropriately seeking more medication because their pain is being under-treated.

...Most of the data on physician prescribing patterns show that most physicians under-prescribe medication. At the other end of the spectrum, a few physicians prescribe inappropriately large amounts of pain medications."

The tendency to under-prescribe results in suffering that could be avoided (or at least reduced). Shamans' over-valuing of abstinence can also cause suffering. Many recovering addicts have been instructed by shamans to avoid drugs at any cost. The zealous application of this belief has resulted in many recovering addicts removing themselves from medications that actually contributed to their recovery (i.e. psychotropic medications). Addicts, who clearly need to be careful with pain medications, can even use opiates within their recovery framework. As a recovering person, I have needed surgery and pain medications on a number of occasions. While craving was triggered by these experiences, a conscious commitment to full disclosure and external monitoring of the drug use was sufficient to maintain recovery. As a professional, I have helped many clients who needed pain medication for a short period of time. Not a single client returned to active addiction.

Separating addiction from physical dependency is critical to facilitate identification of addictive disease. Confusion regarding this issue has resulted in many addicts, especially cocaine and marijuana addicts, being trivialized and untreated. In my own experience, on more than one occasion, I have heard stories of marijuana addicts who lied to receive treatment services. Treatment personnel would dismiss the severity of their dilemma until they would fabricate stories that included use of other drugs. Likewise, in recent memory, cocaine was considered to be non-addictive because of the lack of an observable physical dependency phenomenon.

The primary characteristic of addiction does not center on the amount of drug consumed, nor on the presence of physical dependency, but instead on

> *"The observation of one or more of its characteristic features: impaired control, craving and compulsive use, and continued use despite negative physical, mental and /or social consequences."*[5]

A Working Definition

The above definitions reflect the current scientific understanding of addiction and accurately reflect the experience reported by my addicted clients. A briefer version of this definition, including a summary of the core characteristics described by the phrase loss of control (LoC) is the definition that I find has the most clinical and instructional utility:

> Addiction: The chronic, usually progressive, sometimes fatal disease that is characterized by the loss of control (LoC) over the consumption of mood-altering drugs.

The basic characteristic of addiction is the LoC phenomenon. LoC refers to using beyond intent and/or use despite negative consequences. LoC causes the addict to experience a conflict between his or her behavior (using) and his or her values.

Understanding addiction from the inside out

I have taught a course entitled, AD 101 Alcohol Use and Addiction, for 15 years. Teaching this class has taught me that the concept of LoC is often elusive for my non-recovering students. They often confuse LoC with doing bizarre things while drunk, believing that being out of control is synonymous with LoC. Sometimes they believe that LoC is something that happens every time the person uses, instead of an unpredictable event for all but the very severe addict. I have had the most success communicating the reality of LoC by asking students to complete the following five-step exercise:

1) List the 6 most important things to you in the world.

2) Now imagine a scenario in which you use more than you intend and your use caused you to jeopardize your own values.

3) Now imagine how you would feel and what you would tell yourself about having allowed this type of event to occur.

4) Now imagine a scenario in which your using, once again, caused you to jeopardize this value.

5) Now imagine having many successful using experiences where LoC was not experienced. What would you tell yourself about your using now?

To understand addiction is to understand that addicts are people who are in conflict with themselves. Their use will unpredictably extend beyond their original intent and they will pay a price they do not want to pay. LoC happens over time, not every time. LoC will result in significant emotional discord.

Diagnosis of Addiction: LoC and the DSM IV Criteria

Confusion regarding the diagnosis of addiction is still very common. Much of the confusion stems from the old belief that in order to be an addict, one had to be physically dependent on the drug. Some of this confusion has been addressed by the commonly used Diagnostic and Statistical Manual (DSM IV)6, which includes sub typing dependence "with physiological dependence" and "without physiological dependence." (The DSM IV uses the phrase "substance dependence" rather than "addiction"). Note that one can be physiologically dependent and not meet the criteria for substance dependence.

The DSM IV Criteria

A maladaptive pattern of substance use, leading to clinically significant impairment or distress, as manifested by three (or more) of the following, occurring at any time in the same 12-month period:

1) Tolerance, as defined by either of the following:
a) A need for markedly increased amounts of the substance to achieve intoxication or desired effect
b) Markedly diminished effect with continued use of the same amount of the substance

2) Withdrawal, as manifested by either of the following:
a) The characteristic withdrawal syndrome for the substance
b) The same (or closely related) substance is taken to relieve or avoid withdrawal symptoms

3) The substance is often taken in larger amounts or over a longer period than was intended.

4) There is a persistent desire or unsuccessful efforts to cut down or control substance use

5) A great deal of time is spent in activities necessary to obtain the substance (e.g., chain-smoking) or recover from its effects

6) Important social, occupational, or recreational activities are given up or reduced because of substance use

7) The substance use is continued despite knowledge of having a persistent or recurrent physical or psychological problem that is likely to have been caused or exacerbated by the substance (e.g., current cocaine use despite recognition of cocaine-induced depression, or continued drinking despite recognition that an ulcer was made worse by alcohol consumption).

Note that Criteria 3 -7 will almost always involve some form of LoC and that if the counselor finds several examples of LoC, the client will undoubtedly meet the criteria for substance dependence. Emphasis toward LoC instead of on physiological dependence has allowed cocaine and marijuana addiction to be identified. Not long ago, these drugs had been thought of as "only" being *psychologically* addictive. As we developed an increasing understanding of neurochemistry and the functioning of the brain, it has become clear that to make a firm distinction between psychological and physiological is actually quite absurd. At the risk of confusing matters, as we understand more and more about neurochemistry, it becomes clear that all addiction is, at least in part, physiological; that is, it involves specific regions of the brain and various neurochemical pathways. The reality then is that some addicts are physically dependent and some are not, but all addictions have physiological underpinnings. LoC is the core identifying feature of addiction. Addiction is a brain disease.

Dangerous Tides

I have been concerned for many years that the fundamentals of addiction treatment have been eroding and slowly being replaced by a set of beliefs and values that are potentially very dangerous for addicted clients. It seems that addiction treatment has, far too often, evolved into a discipline that portrays addiction as secondary to some greater underlying disorder. Treatment then becomes an exercise where identification and addressing of this underlying disorder is prioritized. Exploration of the individual's experience of LoC is either de-emphasized or absent. As evidenced by my experience with addiction educators in the State of Oregon, as mentioned (in the previous chapter), many professionals in the addiction counseling-community believe that LoC is a myth. This trend seems to be significant and growing. Additional evidence of this trend comes from examining and/or attending the plethora of addiction related trainings available. In my experience, it is very rare to go to a conference or major presentation where LoC is even mentioned.

LoC is not a concept but rather a reality that has been defined millions of times in the lives of human beings and has left a trail of carnage and trauma in its wake. Alcoholics who try to be social drinkers can be deadly to themselves and to others. Alcoholics who attempt to control their drinking will eventually, with rare exception, fail.

Consider the case of Audrey Kishline, the author of *Moderate Drinking* and founder of Moderation Management. Her program formed a national movement, which uses a 9-step program designed to help people control their drinking. Her nine-step program failed to control her drinking. Audrey Kishline drank, got drunk, drove her car, and killed two people in a drunk driving accident. She has since recanted her earlier philosophy by stating to a reporter "her moderate-drinking program had been nothing but a way for her to deny her problem drinking." [7]

Addicts who attempt to control their use are playing with a loaded gun. A treatment industry that encourages addicts to consider controlled using is at best naïve and at worse complicit in the devastation that will surely follow.

Let's examine this controlled-using strategy through the lens of nicotine addiction. How realistic would it be to attempt to teach a 1-to-2 pack-a-day smoker to be a controlled smoker? Most smokers have tried to control their use but without success. No one with even scant knowledge of nicotine addiction would ethically propose a controlled-smoking strategy for the nicotine addict. Certainly there exists some individuals who smoke in a non-addictive manner and who may be controlled smokers, but taking someone who is clearly addicted and attempting to teach them controlled smoking will almost always result in failure.

Therapeutic Controlled-Using Strategies

It may seem a bit absurd to read the section title, *Therapeutic Controlled Using Strategies* after my near rant about the devastating consequences that can result from addicts trying to be controlled users. It may be helpful to point out that almost all addicts try to control their use. The point of this section is to illuminate the reality that addicts will try to control their use and that helping them think about what they are doing can be very helpful.

Consider that even the "Big Book" of Alcoholics Anonymous suggests that trying controlled drinking can be useful:

> *"We do not like to pronounce any individual as alcoholic, but you can quickly diagnose yourself. Step over to the nearest bar room and try some controlled drinking. Try to drink and stop abruptly. Try it more than once. It will not take long for you to decide, if you are honest with yourself about it. It may be worth a bad case of jitters if you get a full knowledge of your condition."*[8]

A controlled-drinking/using strategy can be used ethically by a professional when the individual is truly unclear about their relationship with mood altering chemicals or when their problematic use is secondary to another issue (i.e. unmanaged stress coupled with a deficiency of skills to address the stress, and with only evidence of abuse and not addiction present). Most people who think they can control their use will try to do so. Controlled-using strategies can be used as a diagnostic tool for addicts and as an alternative to abstinence for the abuser.

While it may sound obvious, it is important to understand that in order to use a controlled-using trial to determine if LoC is present, one needs to use. Many addicts will use periods of abstinence to prove they can control their use. One of my own family members would stop drinking for a year at a time, every other year (starting or stopping drinking on January 1st) for 10 years. In his mind, his not drinking was proof he could control his drinking. What he failed at the time to understand, is that it is not what happens when he isn't drinking, but what happens when he is drinking that is the key to revealing addiction. Now that he is in recovery, he describes his non-drinking episodes as his "alcoholic denial years."

Attachment to abstinence as "proof" of not having a problem is actually indicative of addiction (or a least a strange relationship with mood altering chemicals). Imagine if someone announced that they have now been off of beets for 3 months. Doesn't this suggest that there must be some reason, some difficulty in their relationship with beets, to make this an important occurrence? Normal beet eaters don't need to make the proclamation that they are now beet free. When someone uses a period of abstinence to define him or her self as not having a problem, it is very useful to inquire about what motivated them to become abstinent in the first place. Abstinence can be used as "proof" that one is in "control" and can serve to avoid realization that LoC is inevitable once using has been re-engaged in.

When using a controlled-using strategy it is essential that limits be established for how often the person will use, how much he will use on those days he uses, and how many times he can fail in his attempts to control his use before changing his goal to abstinence. The parameters of controlled using are not particularly useful when imposed by an external source but rather need to be created and "owned" by the individual questioning his use. It is also important to educate the individual about LoC as the central identifying feature of the addictive experience. The counselor's task in this approach is to help the client build a self-diagnosis mechanism and to facilitate the continued conscious examination of the client's experience with mood-altering drugs. While it is important to note that this approach can be dangerous in terms of the possible negative consequences often incurred with LoC, the counselor is not actually recommending the controlled-drinking experiment but rather is responding to the individual **who is planning to use anyway**. Often, but certainly not always, a single serious controlled-using trial is sufficient to prove whether the client can reliably control her use or whether she should pursue abstinence. One of the greatest challenges for counselors (especially shamans) working with this type of individual is to be able to authentically embrace the legitimacy of this endeavor, while they pursue clarity and accept that controlled use may be an actual possibility for the client. While further exploration of controlled-using strategies goes beyond the intent of this work, it is important to note that alcohol and drug abusers may certainly benefit from the growing number of self-help manuals and counseling strategies that address controlled using.

Historically, shamans have tended toward over-diagnosis of addiction and a low tolerance for controlled-using strategies. I have worked in facilities, where the only criteria for diagnosis were the person's presentation for an intake. If they did not reveal significant information that would support a diagnosis of addiction, then they would be labeled as in denial, which would then be used to support a diagnosis of addiction. Few addicts are motivated by an externally mandated diagnosis. This position, ironically, likely interferes with those who need to move into recovery by prematurely trying to force them to do so and prevents abusers from learning healthy patterns if the only option they have to choose from is abstinence.

Diagnosis of addiction should arise from a co-operative effort that places priority on the subjective experience of the client. The diagnosis should include specific and concrete examples of LoC that support the individual's acquisition of an intrinsic motivation to address their relationship with mood-altering chemicals.

Trail of Tears

It is one thing to respond to a client's presentation that clearly delineates her plan to continue to use with a suggestion of a controlled-using experiment, but it is a completely different issue when a counselor proposes that she attempt controlled-using despite a clear history of

LoC. One of the most often cited studies that claimed to support the practice of teaching alcoholics to be controlled drinkers was conducted by Mark and Linda Sobell in 1978 (by their own acknowledgement, these priests had absolutely no experience treating alcoholics prior to this experiment.) The published results of their study stated that they successfully treated physically dependent, chronic alcoholics to return to controlled moderate drinking. The Sobells claimed that they had trained 20 alcoholic men to become social drinkers: "...many engaged in limited, non-problem drinking throughout the follow up period."[9] In a 10-year follow-up to the Sobells' research conducted by Maltzman, Pendery, and West,[10] it was discovered that with the exception of one patient whose initial diagnosis was questioned, all had been drinking alcoholically, with multiple hospitalizations and incarcerations. Four had died of alcohol-related causes, another had disappeared while drinking, and six had resorted to programs of total abstinence.[11] Despite the follow-up study, Sobells' work is still cited as evidence that controlled drinking is a legitimate goal for alcoholics. Despite research by prestigious alcoholism authorities, like Griffith Edwards who concluded in 1994 that research disproved the Sobell's position, the scientism that supports the dogma that controlled drinking is a realistic goal for alcoholics remains strong.[12] Consider that one researcher, Ewing in 1975, was determined to prove that alcoholics could indeed become controlled drinkers. He used a wide array of behavioral modification techniques in his quest. After careful and lengthy follow-up, at the end of four years he cancelled the experiment because <u>every one of his subjects</u> had failed to remain a controlled drinker.[13] In 1985, Helzer and Associates studied five- and seven-year outcomes of 1,289 diagnosed and treated alcoholics. They found that 1.6% were successful moderate drinkers.[14] Could any ethical professional actually propose a treatment goal that had a failure rate of 98.4%?

Attempts to teach controlled drinking among less severe problem-drinkers has persisted among behavioral researchers over decades, with a small proportion of those treated (less than 20%) able to successfully learn controlled drinking.15 Given the diagnostic challenge of determining who is actually addicted and who has not "crossed the line," then a success rate of only 20% with the "less severe problem drinkers" does not provide any meaningful evidence that controlled-drinking/using strategies is a reasonable and responsible recommendation for an addict.

While controlled drinking is certainly a possibility for some individuals who abuse alcohol, it is not a reasonable suggestion for individuals who are alcoholic. This is not to say that one should simply tell problem drinkers (including alcoholics) that he or she needs to abstain from drinking. Individuals who continue to believe that they may be able to control their using are unlikely to consider a goal of abstinence regardless of the advice of others. With my work with physicians, those who have returned to use despite the reality that their use would jeopardize their medical license (or at least result in severe sanctions), always report the same thing: they used because they thought they could. The decision to adopt a long-term goal of abstinence requires that the individual be completely convinced by his or her own experience that they cannot control their use; otherwise, they are likely to continue to strive for control. This has significant implications for treatment, and is consistent with the AA belief that the individual must be convinced and admit that they are not able to control drinking (powerlessness) in order to successfully engage in abstinence.

The Problem with Motivational Interviewing

The single most popular training I have seen in recent years at addiction-specific conferences revolves around the work of Miller and Rollnick in *Motivational Interviewing: Preparing People to Change Addictive Behavior.*

While I appreciate their work from a general counseling perspective, I believe it is seriously flawed in terms of application to counseling addicts. The flaw that concerns me involves one issue: LoC. They believe LoC does not exist. From their book:

> ..."*That is, experiences and behaviors that follow ordinary principles of psychology are mistakenly interpreted as special symptoms indicative of unique addictive pathology (e.g., denial, craving, loss of control).*"[16]

This is the only reference to LoC in their entire text. Clearly, the authors of this text do not believe that the core identifying feature of addiction is LoC. Consider for a moment that they are correct, that LoC is a myth. Addicts then should have the ability to have power over their addiction. We should see a large majority of addicts presenting for treatment successfully learning to become controlled users. Yet, this is not the case. Instead we have a very small minority of people presenting for treatment demonstrating an ability to learn to be controlled users. If addiction is curable by utilization of a specific counseling approach, we have yet to discover that counseling approach.

These authors' failure to include LoC in their approach to counseling greatly weakens the effectiveness of Motivational Interviewing when applied to addiction. In their own words they state that:

> *"The question, then, is this: What are the most effective ways for helping people to examine and accept reality, particularly uncomfortable reality?"*[17]

My question to these authors is how can one help someone else accept a reality that they themselves refuse to embrace? Millions of people who have achieved sobriety through Alcoholics Anonymous have done so by embracing the reality of their being powerless over alcohol. It appears that these authors are suggesting that these millions of people are actually incorrect in their thinking, that they aren't really powerless. It is unclear what reality these authors would have them embrace.

It is my firm belief that if you want to help addicts accept their reality, then you need to have a sophisticated understanding of the expression of LoC in the real world of addicts. Furthermore, it is equally vital to be able to recognize the self-betrayal that arises from LoC if you wish to offer a compassionate and potentially helpful response to someone struggling with addiction.

Bottom Line Beliefs

1) <u>Acceptance and understanding of LoC is essential to the ethical practice of addiction counseling</u>.

In the words of Stephanie Brown, *Treating the Alcoholic - A Developmental Model of Recovery*:

> *"So what is the place for psychotherapy in the treatment of alcoholism? There is no relevant place unless the therapist can alter basic beliefs. Therapist must recognize loss of control for the alcoholic and must accept their own total lack of control in being able to make the patient change. Therapists who recognize their own limits can then begin to help the alcoholic accept the diagnosis of alcoholism, the lack of control that goes with it, and the abstinence required. The therapist can then help the patient learn how to stay abstinent."*[18]

2) <u>Not everyone who has a concern with their use of mood-altering drugs is an addict</u>.

Over-diagnosis of addiction has certainly occurred in many treatment centers and is a reality not to be denied. The ethical counselor needs to be open to the possibility that their client may or may not be addicted; they may or may not have a history of LoC. As awareness about addiction has dramatically increased in the last few decades, the sensitivity to the presence of addiction has resulted in a "raising of the bottom" (the point at which we can recognize that a user has crossed the line into addiction). An additional result of this consciousness shift is a significant increase in the individuals, who may or may not be addicts, who are presenting to the addiction counseling community. Attempting to force everyone who presents for services into an abstinence track is to underestimate the powerful consciousness shift that has occurred, and it can alienate and prevent an individual from getting the help they desperately need.

Once someone "crosses the line" from abuse into addiction, it is very likely they will experience LoC when they consume mood-altering chemicals. This is not to say that LoC happens every time, but over time. Many addicts can control their use for periods of time and perhaps even most of the time. It is not the 9 out of 10 times they control their use that is important but the 1 out of 10 times that they don't! Addicts can control their use in specific situations and for various time periods and will often do so to prove that they do not have a 'problem.' It is also common for addicts to quit using to prove they don't have a problem.

3) Determining why someone uses mood-altering chemicals is not particularly useful in understanding addiction.

Decades of research attempting to identify and describe the underpinnings of the "addictive personality" have failed to result in a meaningful accumulation of evidence.[19] Viewing addiction as secondary to some underlying psychological disorder is simply not supported by evidence, and such a view can be injurious to the addict seeking help. Countless addicts have gone to counselors for depression, marriage problems, anxiety issues, etc., and have never even been asked about their relationship with mood-altering chemicals! When the using has been identified, it has often been construed as a result of the other unresolved issue and never directly addressed. On the other hand, the situations that are likely to prompt a using response (or any co-occurring disorder) can be an important component of a recovery strategy and may in fact need to be addressed simultaneously. Once the addiction has been identified and addressed, the individual recovering person needs to address the "why I use" in order to develop alternatives to using.

4) The primary goal of treatment should be to help the addicted individual discover and explore their personal history with LoC.

Motivation to address their addiction will stem directly from becoming conscious of their internal conflicts due to LoC coupled with the belief they can recover. The perception of hope is as essential to recovery as is the recognition of powerlessness over the ability to consistently control the use of the substance in question.

Addicts have highly developed denial systems

A basic tenet of *Motivational Interviewing* appears to state that denial is a myth.

According to the authors of *M.I.*:

> *"To summarize, research does not support the belief that there is a common personality core or set of robust defenses that is characteristic of people suffering from alcohol and other drug abuse."* [20]

My own professional experiences with addiction has provided countless examples of how addicts can employ any number of internal states in order to avoid facing the reality of their behavior. Addicts will typically find someone else to blame for their using (scapegoating) or find a way to explain how their use is "not that bad" (rationalizing) or emphasizing successful areas of their life as a means of avoiding the actual cost of their use (minimizing). Addicts will project their internal conflicts onto others in their lives or simply keep any conflict about their use at the unconscious level. So are the authors of *M.I.* wrong? Perhaps my experiences are so shrouded by my own belief system that I create the denial I see in my clients?

Despite appearances to the contrary, I actually agree with the understanding that there is not a "common personality core or set of robust defenses that is characteristic of people suffering from alcohol and other drug abuse." This is not to say that denial is a myth but that addicts use the same set of defenses that non-addicts use to manage their internal conflicts. To be in denial simply means to not have full consciousness of the reality of one's situation. Every human being appears fully equipped to use denial for a host of problems. The addict is not a special case; she is another human being who is not fully conscious. Denial is the psychological process that we employ to temporarily avoid psychological pain. The addict's primary source of psychological pain is the conflict they experience between their behavior (LoC) and their values. Denial provides a means to make unacceptable behavior explainable or at least tolerable within the psychological world of the individual experiencing the conflict. An addict's denial system may have many faces but it has one basic function: to remove the addict's awareness of the conflict between her values and her behavior. Stephanie Brown:

> *"The denial of alcoholism is a cognitive phenomenon, which I have referred to as a thinking disorder. Unless the process of denial is unraveled so that the individual can accept the reality of loss of control, behavioral attempts will necessarily be temporary, stopgap measures, designed to gain control with a return to drinking anticipated."*[21]

Thus, identification and deconstruction of the thinking errors that evolved to support the addicted behavior is a critical component of recovery. The following is an example of how allowing the truth of one's behavior to be revealed, unveiling the addicted heart, is an indispensable step in recovery.

The novelist Fyodor Dostoevsky was addicted to gambling. In a letter to his wife about his awakening from his addiction he wrote:

> *"Anna, Anna, you must understand that I am not just an unscrupulous creature - I am a man devoured by the passion for gambling. But I want you to know that now that mirage has been dispersed once and for all and I feel I have been released from this delusion."*[22]

Very similar to the process of denial is the concept of the shadow as elucidated by the renowned psychologist, C.G. Jung. In 1917, in his essay "On the Psychology of the Unconscious," Jung speaks of the personal shadow as the other in us, the unconscious personality of the same sex, the reprehensible inferior, the other that embarrasses or shames us: "By shadow I mean the 'negative' side of the personality, the sum of all those unpleasant qualities we like to hide, together with the insufficiently developed functions and the content of the personal unconscious." By 1945 Jung was referring to the shadow as simply the thing a person has no wish to be. "One does not become enlightened by imagining figures of light," he said, "but by making the darkness conscious. The latter procedure, however, is disagreeable and therefore not popular."[23]

It is by acknowledging the painful repressed truth of addiction, through embracing the inherent conflict that is created by LoC, that brings an addict to their "bottom." This can be a difficult and painful process:

> *"Sometimes the bottom of The Abyss is like a battle-ground, where the soul struggles against possession by monsters of the deep."* [24]

An expression often heard in A.A. is "the way out is through." It is used to suggest that embracing the pain in the abyss allows the person to eventually walk upright freed of the burden of their addiction. British Jungian analyst Liz Greene points to the paradoxical nature of the shadow as both the container of darkness and the beacon pointing toward the light:

> *"It is the suffering, crippled side of the personality which is both the dark shadow that won't change and also the redeemer that transforms one's life and alters one's values. The redeemer can get the hidden treasure or win the princess or slay the dragon because he's marked in some way-he's abnormal. The shadow is both the awful thing that needs redemption, and the suffering redeemer who can provide it."*[25]

Bottom Line Beliefs

1) Addicts, as humans in pain due to their LoC, use denial in an unconscious attempt to make unacceptable behavior acceptable.

Denial is not an all or none phenomenon. Consciousness can surface and then retreat. Humans unconsciously use a variety of mechanisms to remove threatening content from their consciousness. Addicts, due to LoC, experience significant conflict between their behavior and values.

2) <u>Addressing denial can be a very difficult and painful process</u>.

When one becomes conscious of previously unconscious material, a significant degree of angst and despair can be experienced. The very nature of the material that led to its denial in the first place causes discomfort as it is directly addressed. Resolving denial is rarely immediate and complete but instead is more circular and involves a "layers of the onion" dynamic.

3) <u>Resolving denial can liberate energy to aid in transforming the person to their highest self</u>.

It appears that the energy that used to maintain denial can prove to be a wellspring of creativity and vibrancy for living. Denial is inclusive in that it generalizes its tendency to remain unconscious; liberation of the psyche in regard to addiction can create liberation of awareness of a myriad of unconscious material.

Denial must be confronted

Of all the truths that have been inflicted upon addicts by 'helpers,' perhaps the most damaging is the belief that denial must be confronted. The authors of *M.I.* correctly point out that

"There is, in short, no persuasive evidence that aggressive confrontational tactics are even helpful, let

alone superior or preferable, strategies in the treatment of addictive behaviors or other problems."[27]

"Big C" confrontation

Many addiction counselors (including the author) had been indoctrinated into believing that denial is so developed in addicts that "Big C" confrontation (BC) is both warranted and useful. BC is more of an attitude than a behavior. This attitude is basically the counselor communicating, "I will tell you the truth you need to hear." BC is not useful and in fact can destroy the therapeutic relationship and decrease the chance of the client engaging in the kind of self-exploration that increase his consciousness. Unfortunately, many treatment centers have historically relied heavily on this type of confrontation as the primary means of "motivating" clients to accept their addictive disease.

BC also allows an illusion of progress to be created. In facilities where BC confrontation is practiced, it doesn't take long for most clients to understand what the "right" words and behaviors are if they want to be viewed as making progress. Clients will change their behavior accordingly because they want to be viewed as being in "recovery" without having developed the intrinsic motivation that would allow the behavior changes to endure once they left the facility. BC can result in compliance, not long-lasting change.

The attitude that supports a belief in BC is evident in jokes and mottoes that are often found in treatment environment.

How do you know when an addict is lying?
Answer: When their lips are moving!

A sign seen hanging on a wall in a treatment facility:

If the counselor says it remember it! If a client says it forget it!

These examples highlight the underlying belief that the counselor knows what is good for the client and in fact they are more knowledgeable about their client's "truth" than the client is. The BC dynamic gets extrapolated to ridiculous extremes by counselors and facilities who take their position as "the one who knows" to justify all sorts of disrespectful and demeaning behaviors. The following are actual examples taken directly from clients who attended treatment centers within the last few years:

> Length of stay decisions (for clients who can afford longer stays), are made without the involvement of the client. Recovery plans are given to, not created with, clients.
>
> Recovery is something that is assessed without the benefit of any objective measure and without the participation of the client.
>
> How one makes their bed, or conforms with the institutional rules, have been commonly used by many treatment centers as a way to demonstrate the client's lack of acceptance of their powerlessness.
>
> A regular group in this treatment center involves a feedback model that encourages all group members to offer constructive criticism. No encouragement is

> allowed. The person receiving the feedback is not allowed to respond for at least 24 hours.
>
> One client was required to wear mismatched shoes and sox while wearing his pants backwards to help him address his "look good." The treatment personnel viewed this issue and their intervention as directly related to his difficulty in accepting his alcoholism.

When given a safe environment, many people who have been subjected to the prevailing BC attitude will describe how they actually felt while in treatment:

> ***Harold was furious. He angrily described his treatment experience with a red face and increasing volume. "They asked us to share a secret that we had that could interfere with our sobriety. I told a secret that I have never told anyone before. My wife didn't even know. The counselor just blew me off. My secret wasn't apparently the one he was looking for; he really wanted to manipulate the group to see if anyone would admit to using."***

While in treatment, Harold's outward reaction to this event was to turn silent. He quickly learned that it was not his internal state that was valued, but rather his job was to create the disclosures and reactions that were consistent with the belief system of his counselor. Failure to do so resulted in poor evaluations of progress and frequently with the extension of treatment. He learned that compliance was rewarded; failure to understand and correctly articulate the counselor's worldview would cause him trouble. Harold left treatment with a developed ability to recognize when he needed to be inauthentic and to scan his environment to determine the "correct answer" when in the presence of anyone who has power to evaluate his progress in recovery. Harold would often become angry and anxious when thinking about his treatment experience. Talking about his treatment experience in negative terms felt dangerous and caused even greater anxiety for him. Harold suffered from Post Traumatic Treatment Disorder.

Post Traumatic Treatment Disorder

Post Traumatic Treatment Disorder (PTTD) is a term I created. Students, counselors and clients who hear this term almost always react by first laughing, they think it is a joke. The prevalence of PTTD is evidenced in my experience suggests that it is actually no laughing matter. My private practice consists primarily of my working with physicians in a group setting after they have completed a treatment experience. Fifty to sixty percent of my clients will identify as having PTTD. PTTD has the following characteristics:

1) Anxiety related to and stimulated by either recollections of the treatment experience or by coming in contact with someone who is associated with the treatment experience. The anxiety usually is accompanied by a specific fear that one will be deemed non-compliant or somehow not in recovery and will face adverse consequences that may include return to treatment or other significant sanctions.

2) Anxiety about expressing "truth." The client learns to define "truth" as what they believe the coun-

selor wants them to think, feel or do. Clients become particularly anxious when they are unclear what "truth" they are supposed to express at a given moment.

3) Repressed feelings of anger and betrayal. They are often expressed indirectly until the person is in a safe atmosphere that allows identification and expression of these emotional realities. The intensity of these feelings can be significant.

4) Resistance to current counseling opportunities. Meaningful exploration and positive utilization of counseling opportunities is significantly jeopardized until ample time is given to addressing PTTD.

Bob, a new member in my physician group, asked me the following question, "Do you believe that addiction is a disease?" I was curious about why he was asking this question and I was suspicious that this wasn't the real question he wanted addressed. I answered this way, " I would be happy to answer that question, but I would first like to ask you a question. You were recently released from a 3-month treatment experience at a facility where they specialize in treating health care professionals. Did you ever ask this question? What was their answer?" Bob replied that he had asked this question three times in treatment and that each time he was given the same response: that his need to ask this question demonstrated his lack of acceptance of his disease.

He felt that his treatment might have been extended, at least in part, due to this question. Bob learned not to ask that question again. He clearly harbored anger and bitterness toward this treatment center and seemed to really be asking me, "Are you one of them? Whose truth is more important here, yours or mine? Can you handle what I really think?" Although I eventually directly answered his original question, the majority of this interchange involved soliciting from the Bob what he thought, giving him an opportunity to identify, and begin to process his PTTD with other group members.

Resolving PTTD can be very time-consuming. Some groups require using the large part of many sessions to make the transition from being a "good" client (defined in their minds as what they think the treatment provider has wanted them to be) to becoming an empowered authentic participant who can actually benefit from the recovery group experience. The primary intervention to use with PTTD is the same skill to use to avoid the creation of PTTD, empathy. All clients who experience PTTD describe interactions with the treatment center personnel as predominantly I/it. Resolving PTTD will not occur without an I/Thou interaction. Giving witness to the truth expressed by the client, opens the door to healing of trauma and disrespect often incurred in treatment.

Empathy, not confrontation

When accurate empathy is coupled with compassion, it facilitates the evolution of the individual to a higher level of development. Accurate empathy is the ability to communicate to another a developed understanding of what they are experiencing in thought, feeling, and meaning. Many shamans have confused empathy with identification. They believe that saying "I know how you feel" is empathy instead of reporting to the person their understanding of how they are feeling (i.e. you're feeling sad). Identification can significantly interfere with empathy. Empathy is present when one responds to the others verbal and non-verbal communications in a way that validates their experience (which is not the same as agreement). Accurate empathy includes a circular process of either gaining the client's agreement with the counselor's understanding of their experience or a correction of the counselor's understanding until agreement is obtained.

Carl Rogers, the founder of person-centered therapy, articulated and provided evidence to support the idea that accurate empathy, non-possessive warmth, and genuineness are the three critical conditions that one person can offer another that will result in an optimum environment for positive change. His concepts serve as a strong foundation for anyone who wishes to enhance the development and evolution of others.[28]

Confrontation is a means by which the counselor dishonors their client by relegating them to the status of "less than." Martin Buber[29] described this type of relationship as "I/It." The "I/It" perspective results in all beings being regarded as objects, and thus, losing the relationship to the "Thou" the mysterious Other. This approach causes one to lose genuine awe before the mysterious world, to lose the living spirit of presence in the relentless fury of our will to control. Perhaps then, confrontation arises from a need to control. "I/It" serves as a means to maintain an illusion of control. The antidote to BC is simple; BC is simply impossible from the "I/Thou" perspective. Embracing the other within their own world, viewing our contact with the other as a sacred event, serving as a witness to their journey, allows escape from the illusion of the appropriateness of BC.

It is my belief that an essential component of empathy is true compassion for the other. Many counselors can be excellent communicators, in terms of accurate reflection of content, feeling and meaning, but they seem to lack true caring or a desire to really understand the other, there seems to be some sort of energetic awareness between the two people interacting that something is missing. Some part of their soul can sense the distance from the other. What is missing? Compassion.

> *"Compassion can be roughly defined in terms of a state of mind that is non-violent, non-harming, and non-aggressive. It is a mental attitude based on the wish for others to be free of their suffering and is associated with a sense of commitment, responsibility, and respect towards others."* Dalai Lama[30]

Being compassionate requires awareness and the willingness to give witness to another's suffering. Giving witness to another's suffering means being able to truly listen to the depth of their suffering and being able to demonstrate our understanding through our verbal and nonverbal responses.

> *"In fact, in one sense one could define compassion as the feeling of unbearableness at the sight of other people's suffering, other sentient beings' suffering. And in order to generate that feeling one must first have an appreciation of the seriousness or intensity of another's suffering. So, I think that the more fully one understands suffering, and the various kinds of suffering that we are subject to, the deeper will be one's level of compassion."*[31]

Here is where we come back to the importance of understanding LoC as experienced in the life of the addict. How can one be truly compassionate with the suffering of an addict if they do not understand the experience of an addict? This is not to say that one has to have personally experienced LoC, but that he or she be willing to give witness to the conflict that addicts experience when their use causes them to violate their own values. To be compassionate to the addict is to understand that addicts can both love their children, highly value being a good parent, and yet abandon their children when caught in the throes of their addiction. For the addiction counselor, compassion means being able to tolerate, experience and reflect the suffering caused by LoC.

One role model a counselor can turn to who valued compassion is Virginia Satir. Satir is a key figure in the development of family therapy. Satir's genuine warmth and caring was evident in her natural inclination to incorporate feelings and compassion in the therapeutic relationship. She believed that caring and acceptance are key elements in helping people face their fears and open up their hearts. Satir was unique in her emphasis that love and nurturance are the most important elements to bring to therapy. It is important to note that Satir was not generally supported by prevailing scientism; after all, how do you measure love and nurturance?[32]

A Word of Warning

Giving witness to another's suffering requires significant energy. Each individual has a unique capacity to be in proximity to suffering. Knowing our capacity and the indicators that we have exceeded that ability to be compassionate is vital for the counselor who wishes to have longevity in the addiction-counseling field. To chronically exceed our level of bearing witness to others' suffering results in ill health. Regardless of the name it is given, "burn out" or "compassion fatigue" or "codependency," the counselor's overall health and their capacity to help others will be diminished. It is vital that each counselor have a strategy in place to monitor and replenish the core energy that is consumed by the process of compassion.

The addiction counseling profession is not for everyone. The trauma and pain that addicts experience can be immense. Not everyone can consistently give witness to the trauma of addiction. Some counselors brutalize themselves with the expectation that they should be able to consistently be present for clients' trauma when perhaps their own physical constitution and personality are simply not well equipped for this arena. Other counselors fail to acknowledge the price that being in close proximity to others' trauma can exact and they do not develop needed self-care strategies.

Questions to consider:

1) Is being a consistent witness to others' trauma in your best interest?

2) Do you have a developed self-care strategy to keep yourself healthy while working with severely traumatized people?

3) Do you receive regular supervision/support that encourages you to articulate your reactions to client's trauma?

4) Do you have a life outside of the work place that is balanced and cooperates with your need for regeneration?

Bottom Line Beliefs

1) <u>Confrontation as typically practiced in the addiction-counseling world harms, rather then helps, the addict</u>.

BC confrontation is a strategy based upon uncertain origins that, while producing the illusion of progress, can significantly hinder movement into recovery.

2) Post Traumatic Treatment Disorder is a common occurrence in clients who have experienced BC.

The negative effect of BC can extend well beyond the original treatment experience. Empathy and compassion help provide a means to resolve the isolation and anxiety of PTTD.

3) Empathy not confrontation.

Using an "I/Thou" orientation eliminates the possibility of BC. Accurate empathy, non-possessive warmth, and genuineness are critical conditions for change. Awareness of LoC, and how it is experienced in the natural world of the addict, will maximize the empathy one is able to offer.

4) A word of warning.

Empathy is not without risk. Giving witness to others suffering can result in secondary trauma that warrants respect and consideration.

KEY CONCEPTS

Addiction: The chronic, usually progressive, sometimes fatal disease that is characterized by the loss of control (LoC) over the consumption of mood-altering drugs.

"Big C" Confrontation (BC): BC refers to an interaction between the counselor and the client that involves the counselor assuming an "I/it" position (where the counselor is the "I"). The counselor acts as the "one who knows" and treats the client as the "one who needs to know." This type of interaction harms the counseling relationship and interferes with the recovery process.

Diagnosis of Addiction: The diagnosis of addiction is based upon identification of the presence of LoC. This diagnosis may, or may not, include identification of physical dependency.

DSM IV Criteria: Commonly employed diagnostic criteria that use an implied form of LoC. Physical Dependency criteria are used but not sufficient for diagnosis without LoC.

Empathy: Communication that focuses on the accurate reflection of the other's beliefs, feelings, and meanings. Accurate empathy facilitates self-disclosing and self-exploration.

Physical Dependency: The body's adaptation to the presence of drugs as evidenced by the development of tolerance and withdrawal. Physical Dependency is a distinct phenomena that may, or may not, accompany addiction and is not by itself sufficient to provide a diagnosis of addiction.

Post Traumatic Treatment Disorder: A common occurrence in clients who have been subjected to BC. Primary feature is anxiety caused by fear of repercussions. Clients learn to filter their internal world and attempt to express externally "truths" imposed upon them by counselors who use BC tactics. Emergent feelings of anger and betrayal are very common when BC is replaced with empathetic responses.

Summary of Core Beliefs:

1. Acceptance and understanding of LoC is essential to the ethical practice of addiction counseling.
2. Not everyone who has a concern with their use of mood-altering drugs is an addict.
3. Determining why someone uses mood-altering chemicals is not particularly useful in understanding addiction.
4. The primary goal of treatment should be to help the addicted individual discover and explore their personal history with LoC.
5. Addicts, as humans in pain due to their LoC, use denial in an unconscious attempt to make unacceptable behavior acceptable.

6. Addressing denial can be a very difficult and painful process.
7. Resolving denial can liberate energy to aid in transforming the person to their highest self.
8. Confrontation as typically practiced in the addiction-counseling world harms, rather then helps, the addict.
9. Post Traumatic Treatment Disorder is a common occurrence in clients who have experienced BC.
10. Empathy not confrontation is the goal. Using an "I/Thou" orientation eliminates the possibility of BC. Interest in the other is evidenced by use of accurate empathy, non-possessive warmth, and genuineness. Compassion derived from including awareness of LoC will maximize the understanding one is able to offer the other.
11. A word of warning: Empathy is not without risk. Giving witness to others' suffering can result in secondary trauma that warrants respect and consideration.

Sources

1) National Institute on Drug Abuse. Posted at www.nida.nih.gov
2) American Society of Addiction Medicine. As described by the ASAM Board of Directors February 25, 1990. Posted at www.asam.org
3) In a more recent position statement issued by the American Society of Addiction Medicine, the American Academy of Pain Medicine, and the American Pain Society (approved in February of 2001). Posted at www.asam.org
4)Sidney H. Schnoll, M.D, Medical College of Virginia, directly addressed the under treatment issue for pain patients in a column posted at healthcentral.com"Do patients become addicted from too much pain medication." March 13, 2000
5) American Society of Addiction Medicine.
6) *Diagnostic and Statistical Manual of Mental Disorders*, Fourth Edition, Washington, DC. American Psychiatric Association, 2000.
7) Seattle Times, Friday June 3oth, 2000.
8) *Big Book*, Alcoholics Anonymous, Third Edition, World Services Inc., New York, New York, pgs. 31,32.
9) Sobell, M.B., and Sobell, L.C., Behavioral Research Therapy 1973, 1976.
10) Maltzman, I., Pendery, M., West, L.J., Science, July 9, 1982.
11) Maltzman et al.
12) Edwards
13) Ewing
14) Helzer and Associates
15) Miller, W.R. Leckman, A.L.,Delaney, H.D., & Tinkom, M (in press). Long term follow-up of behavioral self-control training. Journal of Studies on Alcohol.

16) Miller, W.R., & Rollnick, S., *Motivational Interviewing: Preparing People to Change Behavior*, The Guilford Press. New York, New York. 1991. pg 11
17) Miller, pg. 13.
18) Brown, S., Treating the Alcoholic - A Developmental Model of Recovery. John Wiley & Sons, New York. 1985, pg. 15
19) Decades of research attempting to identify and describe the underpinnings of the "addictive personality" have failed to result in a meaningful accumulation of evidence.
20) Miller, pg 10
21) Brown, pg 87
22) Fyodor Dostoevsky, The Gambler, trans. Andrew R. MacAndrew (New York: W.W. Norton and Company, Inc. 1981. pg 7 (As reported by Linda Leonard in Witness to the Fire: Creativity & the Veil of Addiction. Shambahala Publications, Inc. Boston, Massachusetts. 1989. pg. 39)
23) As reported in Abrahams, J., Zweig, C., *Meeting the Shadow: the Hidden Power of the Dark Side of Human Nature.* GP Putnam's Sons. New York, New York. 1991. pg.3,4.
24) Leonard, pg 223
25) Abrahams, J., Zweig, C., Pg xxv
26) Rogers, C.R. The necessary and sufficient conditions for therapeutic personality change. Journal of Consulting Psychology, 221, 95-103 (1957)
27) Buber, Martin
28) His Holiness the Dala Lama, Cutler, H.C. *The Art of Happiness.* Riverbead Books, New York, New York, 1998. pg. 114
29) Dalai Lama. pg, 116
30) Nichols, M.P., & Schwartz, R.C., Family therapy: Concepts and Methods, 4th e. Allyan & Bacon. 2001

Chapter 3: The Anchor Point System

Having established the philosophical underpinnings of the APS, it is now time to turn to the specific "nuts and bolts" strategy of the APS. The APS is like a set of possible dance steps: which steps one employs is dependent upon the interaction between both dancers. The APS is a process of discovery, not a series of prescribed questions and procedures. Each interview is unique and will progress in its own manner. While the same dance steps will be used in different interviews, when they are used, how they are used, and what order they appear in must reflect what is occurring with both dance partners, not just one. For learning purposes, individual steps are simplest to present in a linear fashion, but it is important to note that the application of these is anything but linear.

The goal of the APS is to facilitate the client's acquisition of intrinsic motivation to move into recovery from addictive disease. Intrinsic motivation to address addictive disease develops from the client's awareness of how her behavior conflicts with her values. The primary conflict arises from LoC. Addiction is an illness whose primary indicator is the LoC phenomena; thus LoC is the most important diagnostic criterion. Addicts may or may not be physically addicted, and people who are physically addicted may or may not be addicts.

APS requires seven components:

1) Basic Attending Skills
2) Getting Started
3) The Many Faces of LoC
4) Identifying an Anchor Point
5) Information Gathering Strategies
6) Presentation of an Anchor Point
7) The Close

In order to master the APS, you first need to acquire an intellectual understanding of the system and then learn via experience to apply the system. Learning occurs in a reciprocal fashion where intellectual understanding improves skill and skill application increases intellectual understanding. Initially, most counselors are frustrated trying to learn the APS. With study and practice, frustration gives way to mastery. Learning the APS is usually accelerated if the counselor devotes time to memorizing the basic concepts of the system, because trying to recall individual components of the system while in the midst of client interaction (or role play) is challenging. At the end of this chapter is a summary page of the specific strategies of the APS. Students may use this sheet during initial role plays.

This chapter was developed with the following scenario in mind: The counselor's primary job is to address the needs of a client who is presenting for an intake interview regarding a substance-abuse concern. It is not assumed that the client actually has a substance-use problem.

Basic Attending Skills

The APS assumes that the practitioner is a skilled communicator who can use active listening skills proficiently. In order to help a client's self-exploration, the counselor must be able to respond accurately to the content, feelings, and meaning of the client's presentation to facilitate the client's sense of safety and desire to self-disclose.

The counselor needs to have a genuine interest in the world as seen through the client's eyes. This phenomenological approach is the foundation upon which the APS is built. The previously described I/Thou relationship is essential if a counselor wishes to truly enter the world of another.

A counselor's ability to employ accurate empathy begins to earn him the right to enter the client's world. As the client experiences the counselor as genuine and able to understand him, his tendency will be to deepen his self-examination and increase his self-disclosure. The APS requires the counselor use fundamental communication skills as a base.

1) Can you accurately paraphrase a client's statements?

2) Are you able to identify and verbalize a client's emotional expression?

3) Can you validate a client without necessarily agreeing with him or her?

4) Do your responses to a client lead to increased self disclosure?

The counselor who is a skilled communicator is concerned about both verbal and nonverbal communication. Nonverbal communication begins with the creation of the physical space used to conduct the interview. The following questions may be useful to consider:

1) Is the counseling space comfortable?

2) Is the space free of distraction?

3) Does the space support the basic approach of an I/Thou relationship or does it emphasis a power differential between the counselor and client?

4) Are you prepared for the interview in terms of needed paperwork and materials?

5) Is basic human respect communicated to the client: are you on time for the interview, phones turned off, and your undivided attention available for the client?

A Need for Vigilance

There are four main obstacles that can detract from the counselor's achieving an accurate understanding of the client: focusing on issues that are secondary to the client's relationship with mood-altering drugs; an internal reaction to the client's presentation that removes objectivity (countertransferance); difficulty to respond to a client's expression of feelings; and using judgment instead of witnessing in the interview. This section will discuss ways to recognize and respond to four obstacles.

1) Follow the drug

Many counselors are easily seduced by their client into following a path that seems important, but which moves away from the central presenting conflict: her relationship with mood-altering chemicals. For example, the client presenting for an assessment has had a recent suicide attempt and a terminated marriage. It would be easy to consume the interview with exploration of these two issues, without exploring the possible involvement of substance use. If the counselor becomes focused on exploring the feelings attached to these issues, the substance abuse concerns may get placed on the "back burner." Examining why a person uses is useful only if the goal is to identify the function of his using and help create alternative approaches to the problem (i.e. his use is, at least in part, to help him sleep, learning relaxation techniques could serve as an alternative solution to his insomnia). A more useful question is, "why not use" (if the goal is to determine if a client is addicted). Focus on "why not use" automatically includes reference to the relationship with the drug. Emphasis on this question also allows introduction of how others (i.e. spouse, employer, judge) in the client's world have answered this question for him.

While it certainly is appropriate to respond to issues that the client brings to the counseling table, you can best respond to the client by remaining focused on your primary charge for this interview, helping the client determine the nature of their relationship with mood-altering chemicals. It may be helpful to ask yourself the following questions:

1) How can I appropriately respond to my client's issue, and when is it appropriate to return the interview to the substance-use focus?

2) How does this issue contribute to my understanding of the client's presenting concerns?

3) Does consideration of this issue serve to help or hinder the development of a clear picture of the client's relationship with drugs?

2) Too close to home

An issue for all counselors is the "blind spots" that prevent them from responding objectively to what the client is expressing. The counselor's movement from an objective to a subjective position is commonly called countertransferance. The trauma related to addiction can be severe. It can be very difficult to give witness to the pain and grief of the client if the counselor herself has difficulty expressing her own grief and sadness. This is especially compounded when the counselor has unresolved issues related to his own or someone else's addiction. Counselors need to be vigilant for the emergence of their own countertransferance. The mature counselor knows that the question isn't <u>if</u> they will have countertransferance but, rather, how they will remain vigilant to it and what issues/attitudes make them particularly vulnerable to experiencing a countertransferance reaction? Wise counselors have strategies in place to employ when they realize they are experiencing such a reaction. Every counselor needs to develop strategies for responding to countertransferance.

Three strategies to manage countertransferance:

A) <u>Compartmentalize</u>

The counselor realizes that his "stuff" has been triggered.

He gently notices the reaction.

He visualizes a small box and places the reaction in the box.

He visualizes moving this box to the background with the message, "I'll open this box later. I set it aside for now."

He uses a supervisor, or a supportive colleague, to open the box for consideration later.

If warranted by the contents of the box he pursues his own therapy to dampen the power of this issue.

B) <u>My, My, My, Isn't that interesting!</u>

The counselor realizes that her "stuff" has been triggered.

She says to herself, "My, my, my, isn't that interesting!"

This cue signals that it will be useful to explore this reaction at a later time with a colleague, therapist, or supervisor.

C) Body Scan

The counselor realizes that his "stuff" has been triggered.

He completes a brief body scan to notice any particular tension or posturing that indicates a countertransferance reaction.

He brings brief awareness to this body area with a breath and the silent message: "Let it go. Be present now."

The most important issue when working with one's own countertransferance is to allow awareness of it to occur. Many counselors view themselves as static beings and grossly underestimate the dynamic nature of the counseling relationship. Being open and accepting of the common occurrence of countertransferance greatly increases the likelihood she will become conscious of it and able to deal with it in a healthy fashion. It is very unfortunate that what is called supervision in the addiction counseling world is almost always client focused and only rarely looks at countertransferance issues. Countertransferance belongs in conversations with therapists, colleagues, and supervisors.

3) The vulnerable heart

Many counselors believe that to respond to feelings means to ask the question, "How does that make you feel?" Notice this question places pressure on the client to examine his internal state and find a name to describe what he is feeling. When the client has already told you what they are feeling through words and non-verbal means, if you do not respond to his expression of feelings, it suggests that you are less willing than the client to explore feelings. Imagine a scenario where a client has expressed great sadness through words, tears, shaking and sobbing and to this demonstration of feelings the counselor asks, "How does this make you feel?" Counselors have to be willing to be vulnerable by offering to the client a reflection statement such as, "you are feeling sad." While offering this statement is more risky than asking the "how does this make you feel" question (your reflective statement may be off the mark), it allows a more authentic and engaging exchange to occur. Clients consistently demonstrate the importance of needing validation by repeatedly expressing the same feeling until the counselor indicates an understanding of the internal world presented by the client.

The following questions, while simple, can help you assess your ability to respond to the client's inner world:

1) Do you use specific feeling words when responding to a client?

2) Are you uncomfortable with specific emotions and therefore have difficulty responding to them?

3) Are you afraid to be wrong about your reflection and tend to withhold it from a client?

4) Judgment vs. giving witness

Another area that creates difficulty for some counselors is confusion between offering judgments to a client and to validating (giving witness) to their experience. Take for example a client who comes in with the belief that their boss is "out to get them." Some counselors may consider it useful to offer a judgment about the veracity of this perception instead of helping the client explore the thinking and experiences that have resulted in this conclusion. While a counselor will often have an opinion about the client's presentation that may differ from the client's interpretation of the subject matter, the question really becomes, "how does it serve the client to offer an opinion?" Offering an opinion often serves as a means to provoke resistance with the client and interfere with the client's examining her own perceptions, thinking and conclusions.

Many counselors have difficulty distinguishing between validating a client, "You're feeling angry at your boss because you think he is treating you unfairly", and agreement, "You're right to be angry: your boss didn't treat you fairly."

Validation does not imply agreement, rather it allows further exploration of an issue. Refusing to offer validation can result in a particular subject becoming off-limits to further discussion, until the counselor makes a point of returning to the subject, is able to offer a validation, and rebuilds a feeling of trust regarding that issue.

Counselors often make the mistake of responding to a client's inconsistencies or even recanting of a previous disclosure by resisting the client's resistance. Attempting to use power or persuasion to move a client to a particular position usually reinforces the client's resistance. Clients tend to interpret this behavior as judgmental and indicative of an I/It status. Instead, simply recycling through the content area and re-clarifying the relevant issues allows the I/Thou posture to be maintained.

Addicts live their lives while traveling in a mist, a mist of confusion that keeps them from their own truths. Occasionally, a clarifying light will break through the mist and illuminate a treasure trove of personal truth. An addict's greatest hope is to see her treasure and how it is being threatened by her own behavior. One must illuminate the mist, not try and force the mist to go away. One must serve to help unveil the truths that lie inside, not try to convince what truths should lie in side. This process is rarely linear and in fact it is more normal for it to go off on a tangent, circle around, and move three steps forward, two steps back.

The following questions can help you monitor your tendency to offer judgment or to give witness:

1) Which is easier, to reflect to a client what they think or to tell them what you think?

2) Do you find yourself wanting to agree/disagree with your client?

3) Do you understand the difference between validation and agreement? Is it difficult for you to offer validation when you disagree with someone?

2) Getting Started

Starting the Interview

The wise counselor remembers that the initial interview can provoke anxiety for the client. Building relationship and providing a safe environment should be the top priority. The interview is based on the developing relationship between the counselor and client. Within this context of positive regard and accurate empathy, the APS is used.

The appearance of motivation does not nullify the need for the APS

By the time many clients arrive for an interview they have already shifted their consciousness to understand that they need to change their relationship to mood-altering drugs. A client who appears with what seems to be a significant level of motivation is not excluded from the APS. Application of the APS can further a client's progress by clarifying his source of motivation and understanding how his LoC has caused him to violate his own value system. It is also not unusual for treatment-wise clients to appear to be motivated while actually lacking any intrinsic motivation to pursue recovery.

The following is an example of how a client can appear to be motivated but actually lacks any significant intrinsic motivation to pursue recovery:

> ***Skip was in his third month of inpatient treatment. He was viewed by the staff as being in recovery and was a model patient in terms of his ability to interact in Group with his peers. He followed all the rules and did exactly what his counselor asked him to do. Skip was preparing to be discharged within one week to return to his home in a distant town. The counselor who was facilitating the group was not a full-time member of the staff and in fact conducted just one group a week. Today's group centered on a presentation of stages of recovery and began with an invitation for each group member to describe where they viewed themselves in terms of being in recovery. Group members who viewed themselves as being in recovery were asked to give two brief descriptions of LoC experiences that had helped convince them that they were addicts.***

Skip and the counselor had the following exchange:

> **Skip:** I am an alcoholic. I need to stay sober, continue to attend AA, and see a therapist when I return home. I have 84 days of sobriety and I am excited, one day at a time, to receive my 90 day coin.

Counselor: You are really committed to recovery and looking forward to a sober future. Could you tell us about your LoC experiences that convinced you that you're alcoholic?

Skip: I don't understand.

Counselor: It seems that at this moment we are both a bit confused. One thing I am a bit confused about, if you remember each of you who viewed themselves as being in recovery were asked to describe two loss of control experiences that convinced you that you were alcoholic. Skip, let me ask you this in a different way. How do you know that you are alcoholic?

Skip: They interviewed me when I arrived here and they told me I was!

Counselor: I understand that someone in this facility has diagnosed you as being alcoholic. What I want to know is what do you think? What evidence do you have that you are alcoholic?

Skip: I told you. They told me I was!

Despite repeated recycling and multiple attempts by the counselor, this client was not able to cite a single reason that was specific to his own behavior that would support a diagnosis of alcoholism or even the suggestion of a problematic relationship with alcohol. The client's extrinsic motivation (to be in compliance with an authority's expectations) was the only visible motivation for him to pursue abstinence. This client was clearly treatment-wise but appeared to lack any intrinsic motivation for recovery. Why would this client pursue recovery? Does anyone pursue recovery solely because someone else told them to?

Responding to angry clients

It is not unusual for clients to be very angry at the start of the interview. Most clients do not appear for an interview as a result of a sudden insight about their relationship with mood-altering chemicals. Rather, the typical client has been faced with an extrinsic motivator: threat of losing a job, divorce, a legal problem, or perhaps a health concern. In any event, it is common for a client to appear because someone else told them they must in order to avoid a negative consequence.

Angry clients often direct their anger at the counselor and attempt to make the counselor responsible for the interview. Here is a simple strategy for dealing with initially angry clients:

1) Validate their anger

Simple responses such as, "You're really angry that...," "Your frustrated because...," can be very effective and can contribute to a developing counseling relationship. Ignoring the anger often results in escalation and disrupts the building of relationship. Attempting to try and talk clients out of their anger seldom works.

2) <u>Empower clients to make a choice</u>

Most clients who present with substance use concerns are motivated by extrinsic forces. They have usually been given some form of a mandate to get an assessment or face some sort of negative consequence (i.e. a boss threatening termination, a spouse threatening divorce). It is important that counselors separate themselves as much as possible from that mandate. The counselor will best serve the client by helping them address the mandate, not by aligning with the source of the mandate. Asking the question, *"How can I be helpful to you?"* reframes the interview from something being done to the client to an opportunity *for* the client to be served by the counselor. Although this may seem a subtle point, it is essential that the counselor not be part of the "heat." For example: if a client's employer insists that as a condition of continued employment she receive an assessment, then the employer is the "heat." We can simply state to the client, *"Would it be helpful for you to use this time to complete an assessment or would it be better if you reconsidered agreeing to this interview? Perhaps it would be better for you not to complete this interview or perhaps to schedule it for another time."* I am not suggesting that we be naive regarding the power the extrinsic motivator may have in the client's life, rather that we be very careful not to align with that power, and we maintain our focus on <u>serving the client</u>. This must remain the primary focus even though we are operating within the context of the client's response to extrinsic pressures. The counselor's professional and ethical obligation is to serve the client and not the "heat." The wise counselor will remain as independent as possible if they wish to have a therapeutic relationship with their client.

3) Aikido vs. Karate Response

Karate is a martial art that involves attacking postures and strategies. Aikido is a martial art that involves the utilization of the opponent's energy. Subtle turns and maneuvers result in the energy of the attacker being redirected back to them, while the aikido practitioner retains his own energy. Responding to angry clients requires that the counselor be responsive but that she not contribute more energy to the client's anger. Subtle uses of voice tone, posture, word choice, and timing are especially important. In essence, the counselor needs to get out of the way of the anger yet align with the client in terms of helping them articulate and identify their anger. Counselors who find themselves raising their voice, tightening their bodies, and moving towards the position of what the client "has" to do have unfortunately also become the "heat." The phrase, "the best way out is through," can be useful in this situation. Helping the client express and explore their anger rather than trying to block it is almost always more productive.

4) Tell the truth

Some clients, no matter what the counselor does, will not be able to move beyond their anger. This anger is typically directed at the counselor with the basic attitude, "Go ahead, do what you have to do." It is important not to participate because the client has moved into a position where the interview serves the need of the counselor rather than that of the client. Instead, the counselor should tell the truth as they experience it,"You seem very angry with me. Have I done something to upset you? It seems that for whatever reason, I am probably not the person to do this assessment for you. Would you like to reschedule with someone else?" Although it is common for the client to change their hostile posture once they realize that the counselor is invested in both serving and believing them, it isn't uncommon for the client to terminate the interview because the client refuses to recognize that he, not the counselor, has a need for this process to take place.

Determination of Extrinsic Motivator

"What Brings You Here Today?"

The vast majority of clients do not appear in an addiction counselor's office for an assessment without an extrinsic motivator: a spouse threatening divorce, a boss threatening a job, a court threatening their freedom, or perhaps a physician expressing concern for their health. Most clients are not voluntary; the appointment has not been scheduled solely for their enlightened self-interest. Despite the reality that most clients who present with a substance-abuse concern do have an addiction, it is vital not to prejudge clients and assume that we know anything about the client simply because they present themselves. For example, consider the increasing number of clients who because of jobsite drug testing have been required to complete an evaluation. It is important to remember that drug use does not automatically mean drug addiction.

Interventions and drug treatment can be used as a weapon to further a child custody or divorce proceeding case, for instance. Counselors must be open to the possible truth of any story the client presents.

The question *"What brings you here today?"* can provide a wealth of information. The "what" in this question can lead to identifying the primary extrinsic motivator that led the client to keep this appointment. Exploration of the *"what"* can also help identify the values that the client holds dear. For example, if the *"what"* is the client's spouse, then this suggests that the client values the relationship with the spouse. If they didn't, why would they keep this appointment? The *"here"* is important because this is an assessment interview (or facility). Why specifically was the client referred *"here"* (to an addiction-specific facility)? The *"today"* is useful in eliciting a story related to the "straw that broke the camel's back," the recent event that resulted in this appointment being scheduled "*today.*" The development of a detailed answer to these questions is the foundation upon which the rest of the interview is based. Patience and commitment to the value of obtaining the details is an essential component of the APS.

Two questions related to *"What brings you here today?"* can be very helpful:

> ***"What would happen if you didn't keep this appointment?"***

This question often helps determine the bottom line; that is, the primary reason that motivated the client to come. It also can suggest the most fruitful area for the counselor to explore. What *"bottom line"* **consequence** are you being threatened with? What has motivated you to keep this appointment? The answer to these questions usually gives the counselor a clear picture of a least one value that is important to the client. If a client is being threatened with the loss of their job, then obviously their job is very important to them. If it weren't, they could simply refuse the employer's demand. Likewise, if she is threatened with divorce, she must value the marriage. The determination of the *"bottom line"* allows the counselor to begin to explore for the possibility of LoC given that use of chemicals is involved and a value that was potentially jeopardized by that use.

"Does anyone else know you are here today?"

This question is useful in identifying other motivators and also can place a context around the interview. Imagine if a client is presenting at an employer's request. How useful it would be to know if the spouse also knew about this appointment and what the spouse thought about this situation. Identifying important people in the client's life who have a stated opinion about the client's circumstance can be a source of significant information and insight.

3) The Many Faces of LoC

Exploring LoC

Essential to the LoC is the ability to be sensitive to the expression of LoC in the life of the addict. This section is designed to emphasize awareness of LoC.

> ***Bob got off work earlier than expected. He decided to stop by the tavern for a few drinks before going home. He knew that his wife was expecting him for dinner and that they had invited two other couples over for the evening. Bob drank more than he planned, got drunk, and didn't arrive home until 2:30 a.m.***

> ***Sara had decided to party with her friends on Saturday night. She took $50 out of her bank account for the evening. She unexpectedly ran into a friend who sold her some cocaine for $25. Via her ATM machine, Sara spent an additional 300 unplanned dollars on cocaine that night.***

> ***Traci goes to a neighbor's apartment for "just a few minutes" to return a borrowed videotape. Traci's children, ages 4 and 6, were watching a television program and were told, "I'll be back in just a minute." Traci and the neighbor shared a "bong hit" and a beer. Three hours later Traci returned to her apartment visibly intoxicated.***

Bob, Sara and Traci did not plan to get intoxicated. They all experienced LoC. An important distinction between LoC and simple intoxication is that almost anyone, if given enough drugs, will do crazy things. Doing crazy things is not the same as experiencing LoC. With LoC the person's behavior is in conflict with his or her own moral code. To discover if someone is experiencing LoC or is simply exercising a choice to get intoxicated (and perhaps do crazy things) involves focus on the **context** in which the using occurs.

Understanding the context of LoC

Understanding the environment that the LoC occurred within is vitally important. It is the inclusion of this context that allows the conflictual values to be identified.

> ***Bob got off work earlier than expected. He decided to stop by the tavern for a few drinks before he going home. He knew that his wife was expecting him for dinner and that they had invited two other couples over for the evening. Bob drank more than he planned, got drunk, and didn't arrive home until 2:30 a.m.***

Context: Bob loves his wife and is glad to be married. His friends are important to him and he knows that this dinner has been planned for a month. Bob's LoC places him in direct conflict with his own values concerning his wife and his friends. The context of Bob's use makes his loss of control evident.

> ***Sara had decided to party with her friends on Saturday night. She took $50 out of her bank account for the evening. She unexpectedly ran into a friend who sold her some cocaine for $25. Via her ATM machine, Sara spent an additional 300 unplanned dollars on cocaine that night.***

Context: Sara has been saving for a year to go on a European vacation with her grandmother. She makes $10.18 per hour, and she has no other source of income. The money she spent on cocaine came out of her vacation fund. Sara's LoC places her in direct conflict with her own values regarding money management and her plan to have a once-in-a-lifetime trip with her grandmother. The context of Sara's use makes her LoC evident.

> ***Traci goes to a neighbor's apartment for "just a few minutes" to return a borrowed videotape. Traci's children, ages 4 and 6, were watching a television program and were told, "I'll be back in just a minute." Traci and the neighbor shared a "bong hit" and a beer. Three hours later Traci returned to her apartment visibly intoxicated.***

Context: Traci loves being a parent. She thinks the most important job anyone can have in the world is raising their children. She would call the police if she knew of someone leaving their 4 and 6 year old children unattended for 3 hours. The context of Traci's use makes her LoC evident.

Using Despite Negative Consequences

While a single episode of experiencing a negative consequence because of using does not provide a conclusion of addiction, a pattern of violating one's own moral codes does provide substantial evidence of addiction. Repeated uses despite negative consequences results in the addict amassing a history of violating their own moral code because of their using.

> ***Bob got off work earlier than expected. He decided to stop by the tavern for a few drinks before he going home. He knew that his wife was expecting him for dinner and that they had invited two other couples over for the evening. Bob drank more than he planned, got drunk, and didn't arrive home until 2:30 a.m.***

Imagine what it would be like to be in Bob's shoes the next morning! Bob feels very guilty and tells his wife "it will never happen again." Bob talks and prays with his minister and takes a vow that he will never let his drinking get in the way of his meeting family and social obligations. His wife, who was furious with him, threatened him with divorce if he ever does this to her again! Bob has never felt so repentant nor has he ever taken the step of talking with his minister about his drinking. He believes his wife will keep her threat (she has left for a week 'separation' during the last year). Bob successfully controls his drinking for several weeks until another LoC occurs and he gets drunk when he was supposed to be at a family birthday party. Bob is clearly about to face some negative consequences for his LoC that he did not want to experience: his experience of guilt due to the violation of his solemn oath to his wife and minister and the possible loss of his marriage.

> ***Sara had decided to party with her friends on Saturday night. She took $50 out of her bank account for the evening. She unexpectedly ran into a friend who sold her some cocaine for $25. Via her ATM machine, Sara spent an additional 300 unplanned dollars on cocaine that night.***

Sara was very upset with herself the next morning. She cried as she stared at the ATM slips in her purse. She created a new savings plan that would allow her to accumulate just enough money to go on the planned vacation. She knew her plane ticket was nonrefundable and that if she couldn't save enough to pay her portion of the hotel rooms, she would not be able to go and she would lose the money for the ticket. She spoke with her grandmother that evening about how excited she was about their upcoming trip. The next weekend Sara once again experienced loss of control" and spent $250 on cocaine. She no longer could afford to go on the long-planned vacation.

> ***Traci goes to a neighbor's apartment for "just a few minutes" to return a borrowed videotape. Traci's children, ages 4 and 6, were watching a television program and were told, "I'll be back in just a minute." Traci and the neighbor shared a "bong hit" and a beer. Three hours later Traci returned to her apartment visibly intoxicated.***

When Traci's ex-husband called three days later, she was frightened. He told her that one of the kids had mentioned that they were left alone in the house a long time. He threatened her with suing for sole custody of the children. She was very upset and worried that he actually might take the children from her. Two weeks later she left the children for a "few hours" with her parents but failed to return to pick them up until the next morning. Losing custody of her children because of her LoC is now a very real possibility.

LoC happens over time, not every time

A common misconception about LoC is the belief that the addict always, or at least frequently, experiences it. In fact, LoC may be infrequent and is difficult to predict. Any time someone uses more than they originally intended, it is worrisome and worthy of scrutiny. Identification of LoC produces an opportunity to develop within the client a self-motivating belief. This belief arises from the recognition that LoC is causing a conflict with the individual's values. The self-motivating statement elicited from the client is call the Anchor Point (AP).

4) Identifying an Anchor Point

An Anchor Point is a client's statement of concern for their use involving identification of a value that has been jeopardized by LoC. Constructing an Anchor Point is a process in which the client identifies a specific value that his behavior conflicts with because of LoC. The Anchor Point (AP) is created for the client and not the counselor.

The client must "own" the AP or it does not exist; APs cannot be imposed or forced in any way. For example:

> In the course of an interview the counselor is able to determine that Beth values being a good parent. Due to her LoC, she leaves her children unsupervised in a dangerous situation. She realizes that she is concerned about her drinking because it is interfering with her being a good parent.
>
> **The general form of the AP is:**
> You are concerned about your drinking (using) because it is interfering with....(insert value).
>
> **The AP the counselor reflects back to Beth:**
> *"You are concerned about your drinking because it is interfering with your being the parent you want to be."*

Other examples of APs:

> *"You are worried about your drug usage because it has cost you thousands of dollars and has, in fact, caused you to lose your home."*
>
> *"You are upset with yourself because you are aware that cocaine use has cost you your marriage."*
>
> *"You are scared because you know that you have damaged your heart with your heroin use and despite your fear you haven't been able to stop using."*

ANCHOR POINT = Client ownership of value + conflictual behavior caused by LoC.

The process of building the AP is as important as the AP

The purpose of the Anchor Point System is to raise the consciousness of the client regarding their relationship with substance use. This differs dramatically from an interview designed to result in a therapist-determined diagnosis. While the APS will allow the counselor to collect data to support a diagnosis, this is not the focus of the interview but rather a byproduct. The emphasis of the interview is on the client's consciousness, not the therapist's documentation needs. **If the client does not "own" the AP, then it does not exist.** It is common for the counselor to be able to predict (and, in fact, this is necessary) what the AP will be long before the client is able to articulate this concern; however, the process that facilitates the client's acquisition of the consciousness is critical and needs to proceed at the client's pace.

Determination of values

APs almost always involve the same basic value arenas: freedom, health, family, career, and self-respect. The counselor needs to be clear in eliciting the client's ownership of the value. Assumption of a value is at best a very risky position. Clients need to be given the chance to articulate their ownership of a value. Simple questions can serve this purpose:

Do you love your spouse?

Is your job important to you?

Is staying out of jail a priority for you?

How do you like being a parent?

Concise reflections are important to use as well:

It seems clear that you love your wife and that staying married is important to you.

You make a lot of money at this job and you really would like to keep it.

You hate jail and are frightened about the possibility of being incarcerated.

Your children are very important to you.

Careful articulation of values that include clear client ownership of their values is critical to this process.

Determination of conflictual behavior

In order to create an effective AP, the behavior that caused a conflict with a value to occur must be clearly a result of LoC. Alternative explanations for the behavior need to be addressed as they arise in order to facilitate the determining that the conflict between the value and the behavior is directly related to LoC. It is not sufficient to determine that using a mood-altering chemical was related to the conflictual value. The counselor needs to be patient and develop the client's awareness of the LoC.

Most clients are not motivated by theoretical APs (what could happen in the future) but are motivated by examination of events that have already occurred. Three primary information-gathering strategies are used to develop APs: Third-Party Investigation, Decoding and Historical Perspective.

5) Information Gathering Strategies

Gathering information that helps the client explore his or her relationship with using will consume the largest portion of most interviews. This process (as all other parts of the APS) depends upon the counselor's ongoing utilization of basic empathy skills. While this approach is directive in terms of specific questions and emphasis, it is also intended to be reflective and responsive to clients. The right to gather information must be earned by the counselor through accurate empathy and within the scope of the information presented by the client. Questionnaires, or any type of formatted approaches, are not utilized in the APS because they ask the client to respond to an external inquiry rather than present their concerns to a responsive counselor.

There are three different information gathering strategies:

1) Third-Party Investigation
2) Decoding
3) Historical Perspective

Application of these strategies is entirely dependent on the interaction between the client and the counselor. While a single exchange could include all of these strategies simultaneously, each strategy will now be described separately.

1) Third Party Investigation

This strategy aids the client in exploring their presenting concerns without triggering their defensiveness. Once the "bottom line" has been determined, this method can be employed. Questions from this perspective involve identifying the "heat" and asking the client what the "heat" has said to them. The focus is not on why something was said but rather on what. For example, if the bottom line is that the client's spouse has threatened divorce if they don't *"do something about your drinking,"* a third party question would be *"What has your spouse said to you about your drinking?"* Or instead of asking, *"How much do you drink and has it caused you problems,"* the third party technique prompts the counselor to ask *"When was the last time your wife complained about your drinking and what did she say?"*

It is important to emphasize that we are not judging the information as right or wrong. Rather, we are simply trying to determine the full nature of the "other's" complaint. At the same time, we need to maintain a neutral position and be open to the possibility that the complaint is unfounded or that it is more of an issue for the third party than it is for the client.

Examples of Third-Party Investigations:

> *What has your spouse specifically said to you about your drinking?*
>
> *If your boss were here today, what would she say?*
>
> *You said that your family has been complaining about your drug usage. What have they specifically complained about?*
>
> *Your parole officer said you had to have an assessment. What reasons did they give?*

2) Decoding

This strategy is simple. The counselor develops a clear account of the client's presenting concerns by asking specific questions that identify the context and the details of the event in question. He makes no assumptions. This skill is called decoding because it focuses on identifying communication that lends itself to interpretation and needs to be clarified (decoded) to be objectively understood. The decoding strategy moves from the general to the specific. Often a client will imply connections between their using and problems they are experiencing but will fall short of making a direct linkage. Decoding focuses on establishing a direct and specific example of LoC. This requires patience and a commitment to really wanting to understand the world through the client's eyes.

Examples of Decoding Questions:

You mentioned things got out of hand at the party. Can you tell me what you mean by "out of hand?" (Note that "out of hand" could mean any number of things).

I understand that your husband is upset with you because you like to party.

Tell me about the last time your husband was upset by your partying. (The client's general awareness of her husband being upset related to her drinking needs to be developed into the exploration of a specific event that captures his concerns).

You are embarrassed about the recent incident at a church function where you fell asleep in the kitchen. Help me understand how this is related to your wife complaining about your drinking. (The implied connection between "falling asleep" and drinking needs to be explored to determine if drinking caused the loss of consciousness and exactly how this loss of consciousness manifested, i.e. passing out in the middle of a conversation or crawling into cabinet to avoid detection).

3) Historical Perspective (HP)

HP is by far the most complex and the most powerful strategy to use. HP is not to be confused with simply asking questions of a historical nature but instead is a specific multi-step process. The purpose of this strategy is to help identify the specific presence of the aspect of LoC that involves use despite negative consequences. The negative consequences must be defined in terms of the client's value system and directly linked to LoC.

HP involves looking at two separate incidences in which the client violated a specific value as a result of her LoC. Exploring the earliest event often reveals that the client proclaimed in some form, "this will never happen again." Helping the client identify the exact expression of this intent is called capturing the clients mind. Having determined the client's intent after the earliest LoC experience, the counselor helps the client observe how the most recent LoC event contradicts the intent that "this will never happen again." Thus, use despite negative consequences is operationally defined within the real world experience of the client.

The following graphic is intended to help illustrate the application of HP. Notice that the HP strategy involves a circular movement from the present, to the past, and then back to the present. Use this graphic for reference as each step of this process is described.

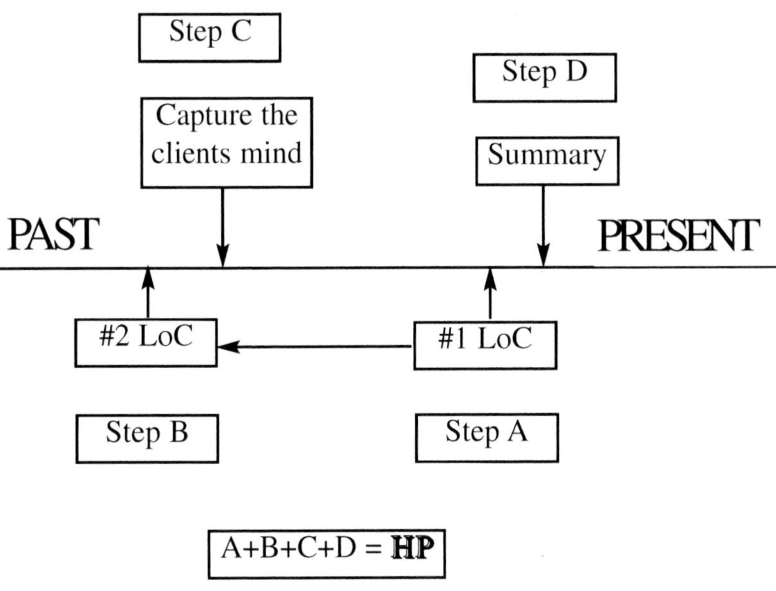

The sequence of strategies that create an HP are as follows:

Step A: Determine a LoC related to a specific value, using decoding and third-party investigation.

Summarize this #1 LoC. For example:

> *"John, last Friday evening you had stopped by a tavern for a few beers and, before you knew it, you had drank to the point of being intoxicated. Your original plan was to be home by 7:00 p.m., so you could take your wife to a birthday party for her mother. As a result of drinking more than you intended, you did not arrive home until after 2:00 a.m. Your wife was furious with you and threatened you with divorce if you don't stop drinking."*

Step B: Determine a LoC that occurred earlier related to the same value, using decoding and third-party investigation.

Summarize this #2 LoC.

Having determined the LoC in Step A, you move to Step B to determine if a previous LoC event related to this specific value has occurred. Note that in the decoding strategy, you move from the general to the specific. Here you move from the specific to the general. If John is asked, "Has this ever happened before?" he could well answer "no" if the situations were not identical. A more general question is called for, a question that needs to reflect the value involved. The primary value, which John had previously identified, was that he loves his wife and wants to preserve his marriage. The following questions would be appropriate to ask John:

Is this the first time your wife has expressed concerns about your drinking? Has she ever threatened you before with separation or divorce due to your drinking?

If the client does report that he has experienced a previous problem related to this value, the counselor returns to decoding and third party investigation to determine how LoC was involved. This step is complete when a detailed description of the event has been developed that includes the client's recognition of LoC.

Summarize the #2 LoC determined in Step B:

Six months ago, you had planned to get home by six o'clock. You had promised your daughter that you would take her to her piano recital. Your daughter and family are important to you and you would never break a promise on purpose. You had intended to have just a few beers with a co-worker because you were able to get off work early. Before you knew it, the bar was closing. Your wife was furious with you when you got home; she left with the kids the next day and did not return for two weeks.

Step C: Determine the client's intent regarding his use after the LoC identified in Step B. This strategy is called capturing the client's mind.

Most people, having violated their own values, will tell themselves some version of "I'll never let that happen again."

From the summary for #2 LoC obtained in Step B, a number of questions could be used to capture the client's mind:

> *What did you tell your wife and family the next time you saw them? What did you tell yourself about your drinking? Your wife and children eventually returned to live with you. Did you reach an agreement regarding your drinking in the future?*

In this scenario, the counselor was eventually able to capture the client's mind as demonstrated with the following summary:

> *John, after this incident you promised your wife, and in fact you intended, never to allow drinking to interfere with another family obligation.*

Step D: Helping the client recognize that, despite her best intention, she did allow "it" to happen again.

If we obtain in Step C from the client some version of "I promised it would never happen again," we already know that it did happen again! The client has now defined "use despite negative consequences" with their own experience.

Step D is a simple restatement of the summaries of Step A, B, and C into one statement:

> *John, six months ago you drank more than you intended and ended up feeling very upset with yourself because you felt that you had let your family down. You were afraid you might lose your family as a result of this incident and, in fact, did live for two weeks with the uncertainty of your family returning. You promised your wife this sort of thing would never happen again. You clearly love your family, fully intended never to let your drinking interfere with being the father and husband you want to be and yet, you recently drank more than you originally planned and now are faced with the fact that your drinking is causing you to jeopardize your family and marriage.*

Step D is the precursor step to presenting a definitive AP.

6) Presentation of an Anchor Point

Emotional Considerations

Presentation of an AP is simply the concise reflection to the client of their own concern about how their using is interfering with one of their values. This presentation does not involve a Perry Mason accusatory style but is a supportive "giving witness" to the client's conflict approach. The apparent emotional reaction to an AP can range from a significant expression of emotional distress to one void of any emotional expression. Many clients are delayed reactors, so emotional reactions can occur hours, days or even weeks after the insight resultant in the AP.

Do not underestimate the power of this process to awaken buried grief and cause significant pain. As obvious as the AP may seem to the counselor, this may be the first time the client has allowed themselves to be conscious of the conflict between their behavior and values. To summarize, you need an attitude of compassion, not conviction, when presenting an AP.

Essential Ingredients

1) Obtain client ownership of the targeted value.

2) Obtain client ownership of the LoC.

3) Present summary of HP. From the previous example:

> *John, six months ago you drank more than you intended and ended up feeling very upset with yourself because you felt that you had let your family down. You were afraid you might lose your family as a result of this incident and, in fact, did live for two weeks with the uncertainty of your family returning. You promised your wife this sort of thing would never happen again. You clearly love your family, fully intended never to let your drinking interfere with being the father and husband you want to be and yet, you recently drank more than you originally planned and now are faced with the fact that your drinking is causing you to jeopardize your family and marriage.*

4) Create a specific and concise descriptive statement derived from the HP summary using the AP basic form *You are concerned about your drinking (using) because it is interfering with...(insert value)* for the client. Applying this strategy to the above summary results in the creation of the following AP: *John, you are concerned that your drinking is jeopardizing your relationship with your wife and family.*

5) Obtain client agreement with this summary. Nonverbal affirmation will suffice: *In response to the counselor's presentation of the AP, the client nods his head in agreement.*

How many Anchor Points are needed?

The number of APs you develop depends on the original goal of the interview. If the goal is assessment and referral, you will want to develop enough APs to support the client's self-diagnosis of addiction while meeting your need for documentation. If the DSM IV R criteria are being used, often one AP can allow you to identify several of the criteria. However, it would be very unusual to have only one AP; most interviews result in at least two to three. Using the scenario developed in the preceding section, note how several of the criteria can be applied:

<u>DSM IV Criteria</u>

The substance is often taken in larger amounts or over a longer period than was intended

> There is a persistent desire or unsuccessful efforts to cut down or control substance use
>
> Important social, occupational, or recreational activities are given up or reduced because of substance use
>
> The substance use is continued despite knowledge of having a persistent or recurrent physical or psychological problem that is likely to have been caused or exacerbated by the substance (e.g., current cocaine use despite recognition of cocaine-induced depression, or continued drinking despite recognition that an ulcer was made worse by alcohol consumption).

If the interview is being conducted from a treatment perspective, more APs will be developed. If treatment involves a full exploration of the client's historical relationship with addictive substances (which, I believe, should be a major focus of treatment), several APs may be needed. The actual number of APs is determined by the client's history and their current ability to identify value-related conflicts due to their use. The goal is not to identify *all* the possible APs but rather to identify those that the client is willing and able to identify at this time. While it is my belief that clients are freed by knowing their own truth, they themselves need to determine how exhaustive their search for their own conflicts because of LoC needs to be. As a general rule, it's best to obtain enough APs so that the client finds intrinsic motivation to pursue recovery but not so many that he is overwhelmed and destabilized beyond his ability to cope. Basic empathy skills will help the counselor discern the direction that the client needs to proceed in this regard.

Temporary Truths

Clients who move into recovery are moving part of their unconscious mind into conscious awareness. This movement is not like turning on a light switch where all that was dark is now illuminated; instead, it is like climbing a mountain where each step gets one closer to the summit. The climber is often fooled into believing that the summit they currently see is the top of the mountain, only to realize from a higher vantage point that this is a false summit and the true summit lies beyond. Recovery, like mountain climbing, usually involves many false summits along the way. Until a higher vantage point is reached, awareness of the false summit cannot be obtained. Belief that the current view is the summit, when it is actually not the summit, is called a temporary truth. Recovery is often a series of temporary truths that reflect the individual's current level of development. Their truth will change as their stability and their capacity to look deeper into their experience increases.

> ***Bill's entry into recovery was triggered by a cocaine-induced seizure that involved his passing out at his work place. While in treatment, Bill became very motivated to enter recovery as he realized the full impact cocaine had on his health, his finances, and his career. Bill was very grateful that his wife was supportive of his recovery and that he***

> ***was returning to a stable home environment. In the first few months of recovery, Bill focused on his health, financial, and career concerns whenever he discussed his addiction. In the sixth month of his recovery, Bill began to examine his relationship with his family. He had originally defined his family as healthy; he was grateful his cocaine addiction had been kept out of his home. He cited the lack of abuse, the lack of using in the home, the material things he provided as evidence that his family was unaffected by his addiction. But now, Bill began to re-examine how his cocaine addiction had affected his relationship with his family. He became depressed and fairly distraught as he realized that his addiction had, in fact, negatively impacted his family in important ways.***

If Bill had been pressed by a counselor within the first months of recovery to do a more thorough analysis of the impact his cocaine addiction had on his family, he might have become overwhelmed and destabilized as a result. Instead, this issue arose within the context of his own development and he was able to address the issues and eventually move to a point of even greater stability.

A challenge for counselors is to support the client who is in the process of accepting and embracing a given truth while knowing that it is very likely that this truth will give way to a different truth in the not-to-distant future. Basic empathy skills will allow the counselor to discern which issues are being offered for examination and which issues are not really open for discussion. The Alcoholics

Anonymous slogan of "First things first" is particularly applicable in discerning which "truth" should be accepted now and which "truth" needs to be pursued later.

7) The Close

The Close occurs when the counselor is confident in the diagnosis of addiction based upon the self-motivating statements (APs) elicited from the client. The intent of the Close is to provide a means of summarizing the interview and providing the client an opportunity to self-diagnose. The close is a fairly linear process and can be broken down in to the following steps:

a) Elicit the "word."

b) Elicit the client's definition of the "word."

c) Build a bridge to a mutually acceptable definition.

d) Create a continuum.

e) Elicit the client's self-diagnosis.

f) Present the Anchor Points.

g) Process emergent feelings.

h) Create an action plan.

During the linear process of the Close, the counselor needs to maintain basic empathy skills and provide non-verbal messages of hope. Hope is communicated when the client is treated with basic respect and when the client is empowered as a decision-maker and a partner in an I/Thou relationship. Hope is communicated when the client's internal world is honored and accurately reflected.

Perhaps most importantly, hope is communicated when the client is treated as a valuable and worthwhile person. Hope should not be offered or withdrawn as a function of the client's goals or perceived progress but should be a consistent presence.

At any time during the Close, the client may need to recycle to previously covered material. This is normal and must be honored. The client's needs and process must come before the counselor's.

a) Elicit the "word"

The word the client uses (or at least is comfortable with) to describe addiction needs to be elicited. The goal is to find common language that is both acceptable to the client and useful for the counselor. There is no inherent value in making the client use a specific word. It can, in fact, be problematic to attempt to force a client to use a specific word. Often during the course of the interview, the client will reveal the language they use to describe addiction. Here are a few examples of how clients indicate their word preference:

> *" Uncle Carl, now he was a real alcoholic!"*
> *" My mom, now there is a drunk for you."*
> *" Joey is a total stoner, a real addict."*

If the client has not revealed a "word" preference then a simple question may provide a starting place:

Counselor: *What word would you use to describe someone who has a problematic relationship with mood-altering chemicals?*

While any language the client uses may be adopted, language that is clearly derogatory may need to be replaced with a less offensive term. The counselor must avoid aligning him or herself with language that demeans the client.

b) Elicit the client's definition of the "word"

Now that we have a word to call "it," what is "it?" Creating a definition of addiction that both the client and the counselor are comfortable with is the next step in this process. Most addicts will have some definition of addiction that does not include their current set of behaviors. Soliciting the client's definition is a fairly straightforward proposition:

The counselor asks some form of this question, "How would you know if someone had crossed the line into addiction?"

Using the previous examples:

> **Counselor:** *What did your brother do, or how did he act, that convinced you he was an addict?*
> **Client:** *He used to have a great job but he lost it. He lost everything: his wife, his kids, his boat, everything. He used everyday and didn't seem to do anything but use.*

Counselor: *Earlier you said that your Uncle Carl was a real alcoholic. What did he do that convinced you he was an alcoholic?*
Client: *Uncle Carl died with nothing but the clothes on his back. He had been thrown out of the family years before, and he died alone. He froze to death, drunk, sitting in a park.*

Counselor: *You described your mom as a drunk. What did she do that convinced you she was a drunk?*
Client: *She was nasty. She would get drunk and have sex with anything that moved. She tried having sex with my brother once. She would repent time and time again, cry and promise that it would never happen again, and of course it always did.*

Most addicts have a definition of addiction that was created as a part of their own experience with the disease. This definition usually allows them to distance themselves from addiction by including behaviors that have not been part of their experience. A counselor must face the challenge of how to build a bridge between the client's definition of addiction and a definition that includes emphasis on LoC.

c) Build a bridge to a mutually acceptable definition

Once we have elicited the client's definition, we must work with it to create a definition that emphasizes the LoC phenomena. This is clearly a process of selective attention in which we bring focus to the aspect of the client's definition that includes LoC. It is not unusual for clients to use extreme examples to define addiction:

someone who has lost everything, someone who uses every day and lives on the street, someone who is dying because of their using. It can be very useful to help the client examine the course of addiction with the example they bring to the table: Was the person always this way? Was there a time you remember when this person worked or was healthy or had a family?

Counselor: *Earlier you said that your Uncle Carl was a real alcoholic. What did he do that convinced you he was an alcoholic?*
Client: *Uncle Carl died with nothing but the clothes on his back. He had been thrown out of the family years before, and he died alone. He froze to death, drunk, sitting in a park.*

Counselor: *Uncle Carl's drinking cost him everything: his family, all of his material possessions, and eventually his life. Was his drinking always as severe as it was in the end? Do you remember what he was like when he was still in the family?*
Client: *Oh yeah, Uncle Carl didn't start drinking until he was 25. He once had his own business. He installed security systems in homes and businesses and did very well. He was an elder in the church. He lost it all.*

Counselor: *Uncle Carl was once a responsible and respected man. It doesn't sound like it was his plan to drink to the point of losing everything. It sounds like he drank more than he intended and ended up paying a price that he didn't want to pay. While Uncle Carl was extreme in his losses and drinking, it does sound like he is a good example of what alco-*

holism is: drinking more than intended and paying a price that he didn't want to pay. Does this make sense to you?
Client: *Yeah.*

Counselor: *An alcoholic then is someone who drinks more than they intend and pays consequences for their drinking they didn't want to pay.*
Client: *That sounds right.*

Here is the bottom line: A definition needs to be created that emphasizes and includes LoC. The phrase "loss of control" itself is not important to use, it is the concept that needs to be included in the definition. The definition needs to be created <u>with</u> the client, <u>not imposed</u> on the client. The final definition needs to be "owned" by both the client and the counselor.

d) Create a continuum

The use of a continuum allows the client to self-diagnose while at the same time distancing them from being as bad as someone else. Not all interviews warrant the including this strategy but it is commonly employed. This strategy is particularly useful when working with a client who suffered at the hands of an addict, for example, someone who was sexually abused by an alcoholic parent. It would be very important for this client to recognize his or her own addiction while maintaining distance from the parent.

Returning once again to Carl, here is an example of the continuum:

Counselor: *Imagine there was to a 1 to 10 scale of addiction. A 1 is someone who has experienced using beyond their intent and paying a price they don't want to pay for their use and a 10 is someone who has lost almost everything, if not everything, in their life due to their using. Uncle Carl sounds like he was a definite 10. Does this make sense to you?*

Client: *Yeah.*

An important element of the continuum is that the only difference between any of the numbers is that it allows the client to distance herself from someone else. All the numbers they could choose from this scale allow them to self-diagnose as addicted. There is no important difference between a 3 and a 4 unless the client ascribes meaning to this difference.

A word of caution. Counselors who are learning the APS make a common mistake that renders the continuum fairly useless: they create a continuum from non-abusive using to addictive using. Within this context, the client choosing a number on the continuum may actually indicate that he does not believe he is addicted. The number they choose has no specific meaning (except perhaps if they choose 10) and gives no indication of their current self-assessment.

e) Elicit the client's self-diagnosis

At this point, we have collected enough Anchor Points to support a diagnosis of addiction. We have created a shared word and definition of addiction with the client, and we have, when appropriate, built a continuum of addiction. While we could offer the client our conclusions at this point, this would be inconsistent with the overall philosophy of the APS. Keeping in mind that it is what the client thinks that is of value (rather than what the counselor believes), the next step is to ask the client if they think the definition of addiction that you have created together applies to them.

If we have used the continuum, this simple question can be asked:

Where would you place yourself on this scale?

If we have not used the continuum, then the client can be asked a form of this question:

Now that we have defined addiction, does this definition apply to your experience?

If the client places herself on the scale, she is saying that she is an addict as defined by the shared definition. The number she chooses is irrelevant except that it allows her not to be a 10.

If the client chooses not to place herself on the scale, we need to avoid the inclination to talk them into the diagnosis. Instead we need to go over the process that has been used so far and identify which part of their agreement regarding the shared definition they have rescinded. Struggle with the client is not what we want to do at this time. Instead we should return to basic clarification skills and focus on reexamination of previously covered ground; this requires patience and tolerance of the client's process.

f) Present the Anchor Points

Once the client can apply the created definition of addiction to his own situation, the counselor's job is to support him in this belief. The counselor can now present the Anchor Points developed during interview as a means of reinforcing the client's self-diagnosis.

Assume for a moment that the following APs were obtained during the body of the interview:

> *You are concerned about your drinking because it is threatening the continuation of your marriage.*
> *You are concerned about your drinking because it is interfering with being a good parent; in fact, you are frightened that your drinking endangered the well-being of your children.*
>
> *You are worried about your drinking because despite your awareness that your liver problems are made worse by drinking, you've been unable to stop.*

With these APs "in hand," the client has made the following self-diagnosis.

> **Client:** *I would say I'm about a four. My drinking has certainly caused me a lot of problems.*
>
> **Counselor:** *You would rank yourself as a four? That makes sense to me. It is clear that you are concerned that your drinking has interfered with your being the mother you want to be. You are also worried about*

your drinking because you've been unable to stop despite your diagnosed liver problems. Finally, you are convinced that your drinking has jeopardized, if not destroyed, your marriage.

Client: *That's the truth.*

g) Process emergent feelings

Remember, presentation of the APs is a compassionate reflection of the client's concerns, not a hostile attorney-like indictment. The more unconscious the emergent APs have been, the more emotional pain is likely to accompany the client's new awareness of their value and behavioral conflicts. This emotional turmoil can range from minimal (almost nonexistent) to suicide. Unfortunately, such suicidal thoughts can result in successful suicides and must be taken very seriously. Do not underestimate the power of compassionate reflection to truly bring a person to confronting themselves. Significant emotional turmoil can result in the commonly reported on experience of a client's feeling worse as she gets better (as defined by having greater consciousness regarding their truth). Individuals who awaken to their addiction often go through a re-examination process where they replay portions of their life through the lens of addiction.

When the client moves from being unconscious to becoming conscious of an internal conflict, it is common to feel emotional distress. In fact, experiencing this emotional distress as an accompaniment to intellectual insight is not only predictable but signifies the creation of a greater conscious awareness. This conscious awareness often becomes difficult to eradicate. AA's folk wisdom say it thus "A head full of AA and a belly full of booze don't mix." It can be very useful for an addict with a freshly acquired consciousness about their addiction to know that this emotional turmoil is a "good" sign, that it occurs directly as a result of their waking up to their own truth and that it is often a part of the process of recovery. In essence, their emotional turmoil can be reframed as a good sign, albeit a painful one.

> **Counselor:** *(To a client who is clearly in distress) You're sad and upset as you recognize and come to terms with your addiction. I know you feel bad right now, but, as strange as this may sound, your feeling bad tells me you're making progress. People who successfully move into recovery often experience sadness and grief in the early phases of this process.*

h) Create an action plan

One of the most powerful things a counselor can do to communicate hope to a client is to act in an affirmative manner, a manner that reflects the counselor's hope for them. Helping a client assess their resources, by creating an appropriate treatment plan or making an appropriate referral, helps instill in the client the hope that they can recover.

Closing Comments

There is no set length of time appropriate for using the APS. One individual may require only one session because she has come already motivated and simply needs someone to give witness to her recognition of her LoC. Another individual may require a substantial amount of time because his process will include needing to test his ability to be a controlled user. The APS is appropriate to use as long as the individual presenting for counseling continues to evidence potential addiction and lacks the intrinsic motivation to pursue abstinence-based recovery. The APS can be placed on hold while an individual embarks on a controlled using attempt, and the counseling relationship can be maintained to help support and monitor the success with this effort. This individual will obviously present a significant challenge to counselors who work in abstinence-based programs.

APS Skill Summary

A) Responding to content - Accurate paraphrasing vs. responses unrelated to clients.
B) Responding to feeling - Offers feeling statements vs. unresponsive to expression of feelings.
C) Nonverbal communication - I/Thou vs. I/It.
D) Does the counselor follow the drug or follow the wound?
E) Does the counselor empower the client or power over the client?
F) Does the provided space/process communicate respect?
G) Does the counselor resist resistance or roll with resistance.
H) Does the counselor give witness or judgment?
I) *"What Brings You Here Today?"*
J) *"What would happen if you didn't keep this appointment?"*
K) *"Does anyone else know you are here today?"*
L) What is the primary extrinsic motivator?
M) What is the bottom line?
N) Who is the third party?
O) Anchor Point -What value(s) have been owned by the client? What LoC was determined that conflicted with the stated value?

P) Third Party Investigation - *What did your boss specifically complain about? Your spouse said you drink to much, can you remember the last time she said this? If she were here today, how would she describe too much?*

Q) Decoding - *You said you arrived to work a little intoxicated, could you tell more about that night starting with why it is a problem to be a little intoxicated at work?*

R) Historical Perspective - *Is this the first time your wife has threatened the continuation of your marriage? What happened? What did you tell yourself after this event?*

S) Presentation of an Anchor Point - *Your concerned about your __________ because it is interfering with __________________.*

T) Elicit the "word." Elicit the client's definition of the "word."

U) Build a bridge to a mutually acceptable definition.

V) Create a continuum.

W) Elicit the client's self-diagnosis.

X) Present the Anchor Points.

Y) Process emergent feelings.

Z) Create an action plan.

Afterword

The APS is very specific in its scope and focus: to help an addict acquire intrinsic motivation to pursue recovery. As an addict is able to understand and accept that he is "powerless," it is very common for him to destabilize and become demoralized. The new awareness that addiction is the root of his problems acts as a light in a darkened room, all of a sudden the room looks very different, the contents of the room now become recognizable. The way unacceptable behavior (LoC) was made acceptable (denial) becomes painfully obvious. Most addicts experience an identity crisis as they face the need to reconstruct themselves. He is likely to be very unstable as he faces head-on the damage of his addiction. While a new set of skills and approaches is needed with a client who has become intrinsically motivated, the essential need for an I/Thou relationship continues. While describing what these new sets of skills and approaches look like is beyond the scope of this work, it is important to note that both shaman and priest are essential to this process. The needs of the early recovering addict are many and a wide array of available resources will provide the greatest likelihood of recovery.

Addiction is a cancer that devours souls, clouds minds, and destroys bodies. To be able to sit with people who suffer from addiction requires great compassion and vision. Vision for what can be, for what goodness can emanate from this being. As we give witness to the pain of addiction that corrupts and warps the truth, we create room for hope to take root. Being grounded in hope provides a way to balance the trauma and the pain most addicts must face in order to recover. Priest and shaman must maintain connection with hope in order to be able to help instill it. The priest and shaman who work year after year with addicts must, first and foremost, have an established core of health and vitality. This core will protect you from being harmed by the frequent exposure to the darkness of addiction. Regeneration of our selves, our souls, and our bodies is essential to anyone who wishes to be a career addiction counselor. May you have the care and compassion for yourself that you daily offer your clients. This field desperately needs compassionate clinicians, priest and shaman alike, who understand addiction and are able to empower their client's journey in recovery. There are many addicts that you have yet to meet, who may give you an opportunity to help save their lives. May you be ready.